Target
Get back on track

1

AQA GCSE (9-1)
Mathematics
Algebra and Shape

Katherine Pate

P Pearson

Published by Pearson Education Limited, 80 Strand, London, WC2R ORL.

www.pearsonschoolsandfecolleges.co.uk

Text © Pearson Education Limited 2018
Typeset by QBS Learning
Original illustrations © Pearson Education Ltd 2018

The right of Katherine Pate to be identified as author of this work has been asserted by her in accordance with the Copyright, Designs and Patents Act 1988.

First published 2018

21 20 19 18
10 9 8 7 6 5 4 3 2 1

British Library Cataloguing in Publication Data
A catalogue record for this book is available from the British Library

ISBN 978 1 292 25802 7

Printed in Slovakia by Neografia

Helping you to formulate grade predictions, apply interventions and track progress.

Any reference to indicative grades in the Pearson Target Workbooks and Pearson Progression Services is not to be used as an accurate indicator of how a student will be awarded a grade for their GCSE exams.

You have told us that mapping the Steps from the Pearson Progression Maps to indicative grades will make it simpler for you to accumulate the evidence to formulate your own grade predictions, apply any interventions and track student progress.

We're really excited about this work and its potential for helping teachers and students. It is, however, important to understand that this mapping is for guidance only to support teachers' own predictions of progress and is not an accurate predictor of grades.

Our Pearson Progression Scale is criterion referenced. If a student can perform a task or demonstrate a skill, we say they are working at a certain Step according to the criteria. Teachers can mark assessments and issue results with reference to these criteria which do not depend on the wider cohort in any given year. For GCSE exams however, all Awarding Organisations set the grade boundaries with reference to the strength of the cohort in any given year.

Each practice question features a Step icon which denotes the level of challenge aligned to the Pearson Progression Map and Scale.

To find out more about the Progression Scale for Maths and to see how it relates to indicative GCSE 9–1 grades go to www.pearsonschools.co.uk/ProgressionServices

Contents

Useful formulae   iv

Glossary   v

Unit 1 Circle theorems

Get started   1
1 Angles at the centre and at the circumference   2
2 Angles in the same segment   4
3 Angles in a cyclic quadrilateral   5
4 The alternate segment theorem   6
Practise the methods   7
Problem-solve!   8

Unit 2 Manipulating algebra

Get started   9
1 Expanding double brackets   10
2 Factorising quadratic expressions of the form
   $ax^2 + bx + c$ 11
3 Simplifying expressions with brackets and
   powers   12
4 Simplifying expressions involving algebraic
   fractions   14
Practise the methods   15
Problem-solve!   16

Unit 3 Solving quadratic equations

Get started   17
1 Solving quadratic equations by factorising   18
2 Solving quadratic equations by completing
   the square   19
3 Solving quadratic equations by using the
   quadratic formula   20
Practise the methods   21
Problem-solve!   22

Unit 4 Algebraic graphs

Get started   23
1 Equations of parallel and perpendicular lines   24
2 Using factorising to sketch quadratic graphs   25
3 Using completing the square to sketch
   quadratic graphs   27
4 Solving quadratic inequalities   28
Practise the methods   29
Problem-solve!   30

Unit 5 Sequences

Get started   31
1 Continuing sequences   32
2 Quadratic sequences   33
3 Pattern sequences   34
Practise the methods   35
Problem-solve!   36

Unit 6 Congruence and similarity

Get started   37
1 Deciding if shapes are congruent or similar   38
2 Proving that triangles are similar   40
3 Perimeters and areas of enlargement   41
4 Similar shapes   42
Practise the methods   44
Problem-solve!   45

Unit 7 Right-angled triangles

Get started   46
1 Finding lengths in right-angled triangles   47
2 Finding angles in right-angled triangles   48
3 Using trigonometry to solve problems   49
4 Using Pythagoras' theorem in 3D problems   50
Practise the methods   51
Problem-solve!   52

**Unit 8 Trigonometry in non-right-angled
triangles**

Get started   53
1 Finding lengths using the sine rule   54
2 Using the cosine rule and the area formula   55
3 Using the sine and cosine rules to find angles 56
4 Using area $= \frac{1}{2}ab \sin C$ to solve problems   57
Practise the methods   58
Problem-solve!   59

Answers   60

Useful formulae

You will need to know these formulae

Trigonometric ratios in a right-angled triangle:

$$\sin x = \frac{\text{opposite}}{\text{hypotenuse}} = \frac{O}{H}$$

$$\cos x = \frac{\text{adjacent}}{\text{hypotenuse}} = \frac{A}{H}$$

$$\tan x = \frac{\text{opposite}}{\text{adjacent}} = \frac{O}{A}$$

cosine rule for triangle ABC: $a^2 = b^2 + c^2 - 2bc \cos A$

sine rule for triangle ABC: $\dfrac{a}{\sin A} = \dfrac{b}{\sin B} = \dfrac{c}{\sin C}$

Glossary

Unit 1 Circle theorems

Circumference: the distance around the outside of a circle.

Radius: straight line from centre of circle to circumference; plural radii.

Sector: the area between two radii, like a slice of pie.

Chord: straight line from one side of the circle to the other, not through the centre.

Diameter: straight line from one side of the circle to the other, through the centre.

Segment: area between a chord and the circumference.

Bisect: cut in half.

Tangent: straight line that just touches a circle at one point.

Perpendicular: at 90°, at right angles to.

Unit 2 Manipulating algebra

Like terms: terms that exactly the same powers of the same letters.

Quadratic expression: an expression with a squared term, and no higher power. For example, $x^2 + 2x - 2$ or $x^2 + 3$

Factor: number or expression that divides into another number or expression.

Unit 4 Algebraic graphs

Perfect square: a quadratic expression $(x + a)^2$ or its expansion $x^2 + 2ax + a^2$

y- intercept: point where a graph crosses the y-axis.

Turning point: lowest point in a U shaped quadratic graph. Highest point in a shaped quadratic graph.

Parallel: with the same gradient.

Unit 5 Sequences

Sequence: a set of numbers that follows a rule.

Quadratic sequence: sequence whose nth term is a quadratic function.

Arithmetic sequence: a sequence where the term-to-term rule is add or subtract a constant number.

Depreciates: goes down in value.

Arithmetic progression: an arithmetic sequence.

Geometric sequence: a sequence where the term-to-term rule is multiply or divide by a constant number.

Ascending sequence: a sequence where the terms get larger.

Descending sequence: a sequence where the terms get smaller.

Finite sequence: sequence with a fixed number of terms.

Infinite sequence: a sequence that goes on forever.

Inverse operation: an operation that 'undoes' an operation.

+ is the inverse of −, and vice versa

× is the inverse of ÷, and vice versa

nth term: an expression for the term in a sequence at position n

Unit 6 Congruence and similarity

Congruent shapes: identical shapes with the same angles and corresponding sides.

Similar shapes: when one shape is an enlargement of the other.

Scale factor: ratio of lengths of similar shapes.

Unit 7 Right-angled triangles

Diagonal of a cuboid: a straight line joining a vertex on the top face to a vertex on the bottom face, passing through the centre of the cuboid.

Diagonal of a 2D shape: a straight line joining two opposite vertices.

① Circle theorems

This unit will help you to find angles in shapes drawn in circles.

AO1 Fluency check

(1) Use the words to label the diagram.

radius   tangent

segment   chord

centre   circumference

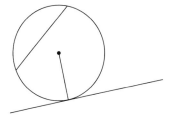

(2) Work out the sizes of the angles labelled with letters.

a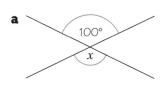

b

c

Key points

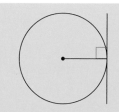

The angle between a tangent and the radius is 90°.

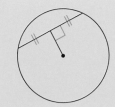

A line from the centre that meets a chord at 90° bisects the chord.

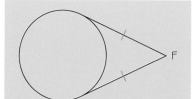

Tangents from a point to a circle are equal.

These **skills boosts** will help you to find angles in circle diagrams.

| 1 Angles at the centre and at the circumference | 2 Angles in the same segment | 3 Angles in a cyclic quadrilateral | 4 The alternate segment theorem |

You might have already done some work on circle theorems. Before starting the first skills boost, rate your confidence with these questions.

① Work out angle *w*.

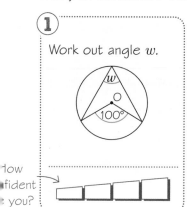

② Write down angle *x*.

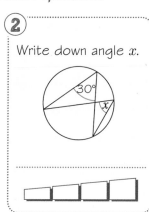

③ Work out angles *y* and *z*.

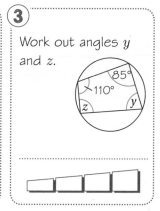

④ PQ is a tangent. Work out angle *t*.

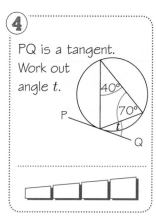

How confident are you?

1 Angles at the centre and at the circumference

The angle at the centre is twice the size of the angle at the circumference.

Guided practice

A, B and C are points on the circumference of a circle, centre O.

∠BOC = 120°

Work out angle a.

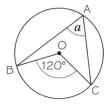

Identify the angle at the centre and the angle at the circumference.

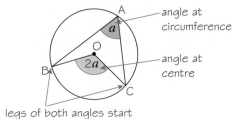

legs of both angles start at the same point

The angle at the centre is .... the angle at the circumference.

∠BOC = 2a

.... = 2a

60° = a

> Write the reason.

> Write this in symbols and solve.

(1) Work out the sizes of the angles labelled with letters.

a

130°

....

b

70°
y

....

c

r O 40°

....

d

s
O
220°

....

Hint The angle at the centre is reflex.

e

125° O t

....

f
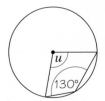
u
130°

....

2 Work out the sizes of the angles labelled with letters.

a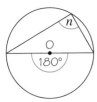

b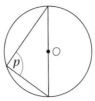

c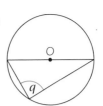

....

Exam-style question

3 A, B and C are points on the circumference of a circle, centre O.

Reflex ∠AOC = 240°

Work out the sizes of angles x and y.

You must give a reason for each stage of your working.

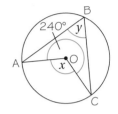

....

.... **(3 marks)**

---

4 D, E and F are points on the circumference of a circle, centre O.

∠E = 70°

Work out **a** ∠DOF ....

b ∠ODE ....

c ∠OFD ....

Give reasons for each stage of your working.

5 PQ and PR are tangents to the circle, centre O.

∠QAR = 50°

Work out the sizes of angles a and b.

Give reasons for your answers.

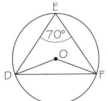

Hint The angle between a tangent and the radius is ....°.

....

6 TJ and TK are tangents to a circle.
L is a point on the circumference.

∠JLK = 55°

Work out **a** ∠JOK ....

b ∠OJT ....

c ∠KJT ....

d ∠JTK ....

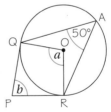

Give reasons for each stage of your working.

Reflect Using your answers to Q2, why is the angle in a semicircle always 90°?

2 Angles in the same segment

Angles in the same segment are equal.

Guided practice

Write down the sizes of the angles marked with letters.

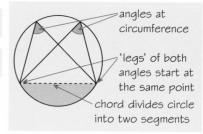

_____

Identify the angles in the same segment.

Angles in the same segment are ....   Write the reason.

$c =$ .... $= 40°$ Write in symbols.

1 Write down the sizes of the angles labelled with letters.

a    b   c

....

2 Write down the sizes of angles r and s.   **Hint** Find r first, then turn the diagram upside down.

....

Exam-style question

3 Work out the size of angle x.

Give reasons for each stage of your working.

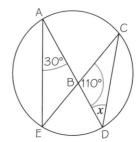

.... (3 marks)

Reflect Does it help to write angles on the diagram as you find them?

3 Angles in a cyclic quadrilateral

A cyclic quadrilateral is a quadrilateral with all four vertices on the circumference of a circle.
Opposite angles in a cyclic quadrilateral add up to 180°.

Guided practice

ABCD is a cyclic quadrilateral.

$\angle ABC = 100°$ and $\angle BCD = 70°$

Work out the size of angles x and y.

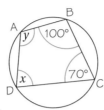

Look for four vertices at the circumference.
Identify the opposite angles.

$a + c = 180°$
$b + d = 180°$

Opposite angles in a cyclic quadrilateral add up to ....°.

$70° + x = 180°$

Write this in symbols and solve.

Write the reason.

$x =$ ....°

................° $+ y =$ ....°

$y =$ ....°

① Work out the sizes of the angles marked with letters.

a

120°
130°
r
....

b

80°
s
95°
....

② In the diagram, OR is a radius that bisects the chord DC.
Work out the sizes of the angles.
Give a reason for each answer.

100°
60°

a $\angle DCB$ **b** $\angle OPC$ **c** $\angle OCP$ **d** $\angle OCB$

....

Hint A radius that bisects a chord meets the chord at ....°.

Exam-style question

③ A, B, C and D are points on the circumference of a circle.

$\angle ADC = 110°$

Work out the sizes of angles a, b and c.

You must give a reason for each stage of your working.

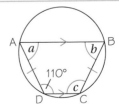
a b
110°
c

.... (3 marks)

Reflect Which of these is a cyclic quadrilateral?

4 The alternate segment theorem

The angle between a tangent and a chord is equal to the angle in the alternate segment.

Guided practice

AT is a tangent to the circle.
Write down the size of angle x.

_____

Identify the equal angles.

$x = 50°$

Alternate .... theorem ◁ Write the reason.

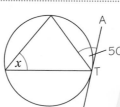

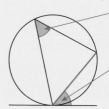

angle in other segment, not on the chord

angle between chord and tangent

(1) In the diagrams, ST is a tangent.
Write down the sizes of the angles labelled with letters.

a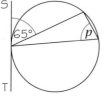

....

b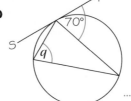

....

Hint

The blue angles are equal.
The red angles are equal.

c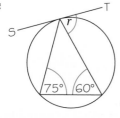

....

d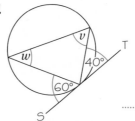

....

(2) PQ and PR are tangents.
Write down the sizes of angles a and b.

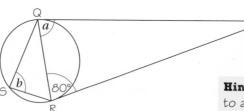

....

Hint Tangents from a point to a circle are ....

Exam-style question

(3) A, B and C are points on the circumference of a circle.
PQ is a tangent to the circle.
Work out the size of angle x.
Give reasons for each stage of your working.

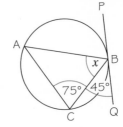

.... (2 marks)

Reflect How can turning a diagram round help you to spot equal angles?

Practise the methods

Answer this question to check where to start.

Check up

Tick the correct statement for this diagram.

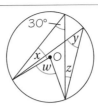

A
$w = 15°$ ◯

B
$x = 30°$ ◯

C
$y = 30°$ ◯

D
$z = 30°$ ◯

If you ticked C go to Q3.

If you ticked A go to Q1 for more practice.

If you ticked B or D go to Q2 for more practice.

1 Work out the sizes of the angles labelled with letters.

a

b

c

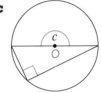

....

2 Work out the sizes of the angles labelled with letters.

a

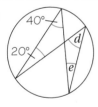

b

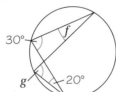

c

....

3 Work out the sizes of the angles labelled with letters. ST is a tangent.

a

b

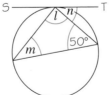

c

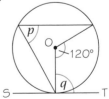

....

Exam-style question

4 PR is a tangent that meets the circle, with centre O, at Q.
A and B are points on the circumference of the circle.
$\angle QAB = 52°$
Work out the sizes of angles x, y and z.
Give reasons for each stage of your working.

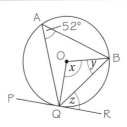

.... (3 marks)

Problem-solve!

Exam-style questions

1 P, Q and R are points on the circumference of a circle, centre O.

Work out the sizes of the angles marked x and y.

You must give a reason for each stage of your working.

(3 marks)

2 This is a cyclic quadrilateral.

Angles a and b are in the ratio 3 : 2

Work out the size of angle c.

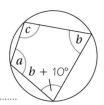

(4 marks)

3 A, B, C and D are points on the circumference of a circle, centre O.

a Work out the sizes of the angles marked x, y and z. Give reasons for your answers.

(3 marks)

b Explain why AC is a line of symmetry of the quadrilateral ABCD.

(1 mark)

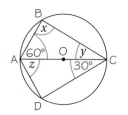

4 A, B, C, D and E are points on a circle.

BFD and AFC are straight lines.

BA = BF

Work out the size of angle a.

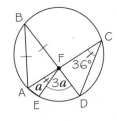

(4 marks)

5 PS is a tangent.

Work out the size of angle c.

Give reasons for your answer.

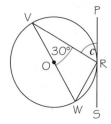

(3 marks)

Now that you have completed this unit, how confident do you feel?

1 Angles at the centre and at the circumference

2 Angles in the same segment

3 Angles in a cyclic quadrilateral

4 The alternate segment theorem

② Manipulating algebra

This unit will help you to manipulate algebraic expressions.

AO1 Fluency check

① Simplify

   a $x^2 \times x^3$ ....   **b** $\dfrac{x^5}{x^3}$ ....   **c** $2a + 3b - 2b^2 + 4a$ ....

② Expand

   a $2x(4x - 1)$ ....   **b** $x(x^2 + 3x)$ ....   **c** $(x + 1)(x - 4)$ ....

   d $-3(x^2 + 4)$ ....   **e** $(x + 5)^2$ ....   **f** $(x + 2)(x - 2)$ ....

③ Factorise

   a $x^2 - 9$ ....   **b** $x^2 - 64$ ....   **c** $x^2 + 5x + 6$ ....

④ Work out

   a $\dfrac{2}{5} + \dfrac{1}{2}$ ....   **b** $\dfrac{3}{5} \times \dfrac{2}{7}$ ....   **c** $\dfrac{3}{8} \div \dfrac{1}{4}$ ....

⑤ **Number sense**

Write down the factors of 24 that sum to

   a 25 ....   **b** 11 ....   **c** −10 ....

Key points

To expand an expression like $(2x + 3)(3x + 1)$, multiply both terms in the second bracket by both terms in the first bracket.

To simplify expressions, expand any brackets and collect like terms.

These **skills boosts** will help you to manipulate algebraic expressions.

① Expanding double brackets

② Factorising quadratic expressions of the form $ax^2 + bx + c$

③ Simplifying expressions with brackets and powers

④ Simplifying expressions involving algebraic fractions

You might have already done some work on manipulating algebraic expressions. Before starting the first skills boost, rate your confidence with these questions.

① Expand
$(2x + 3)(3x + 1)$

② Factorise
$4x^2 + 8x - 5$

③ Simplify
$x(x^2 + 5x) - 2x^2 + 3$

④ Simplify $\dfrac{x}{4} + \dfrac{x}{3}$

How confident are you?

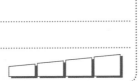

1 Expanding double brackets

To expand double brackets, split them into two expansions.
For example, $(2x + 3)(3x + 2) = 2x(3x + 2) + 3(3x + 2)$

Worked exam question

Guided practice

Expand $(2x + 3)(3x + 2)$

Split $(2x + 3)(3x + 2)$

into $= 2x(3x + 2) + 3(3x + 2)$

Expand the brackets.

$= 6x^2 +$ .... $+ 9x +$ ....

Collect like terms.

$= 6x^2 + 13x + 6$

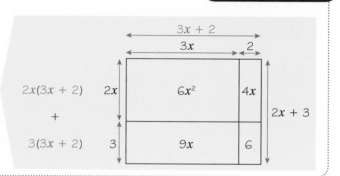

① Expand

   a $(3x + 4)(2x + 1)$ **b** $(2x + 5)(4x - 2)$ **c** $(3x - 2)(4x + 1)$

② Expand

   a $(5x + 3)(2x - 1)$ **b** $(4x - 5)(3x - 1)$ **c** $(5x - 4)(2x - 3)$

③ Expand

   a $(5x + 3)(5x - 3)$ **b** $(4x + 7)(4x - 7)$ **c** $(3x - 1)(3x + 1)$

④ Show that the area of the square is $16x^2 - 24x + 9$

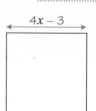

Exam-style question

⑤ Expand and simplify $(2x + 3)^2$

.... **(2 marks)**

Reflect   Why do you think the answers in Q3 are called 'the difference of two squares'?

2 Factorising quadratic expressions of the form $ax^2 + bx + c$

A quadratic expression, like $2x^2 + 7x + 3$, may factorise into two brackets.

Guided practice

Worked exam question

Factorise $2x^2 + 9x + 10$

The expression is of the form $ax^2 + bx + c$
Write down the values of a, b and c

$$2x^2 + 9x + 10$$
$$a = 2 \quad b = 9 \quad c = 10$$

Work out ac.
$$ac = 2 \times 10 = 20$$

Find the factors of ac that sum to b.
Split bx.

$$4 \quad \text{and} \quad 5$$
$$\downarrow \qquad \qquad \downarrow$$
$$\underline{2x^2 + 4x} + \underline{5x + 10}$$

Factorise pairs of terms.
$$= 2x(x + \text{..........}) + 5(x + \text{..........})$$
$$= (2x + 5)(x + 2)$$

$$2 \times 10 = 20$$
$$2x^2 \quad + \quad 9x \quad + \quad 10$$
$$4 + 5$$

Writing the x terms in the reverse order gives the same result.
$$2x^2 + 5x + 4x + 10$$
$$= x(2x + 5) + 2(2x + 5)$$
$$= (x + 2)(2x + 5)$$

1 Factorise

  a $3x^2 + 14x + 8$ **b** $2x^2 + 7x + 6$ **c** $10x^2 + 9x + 2$

  ....

2 Factorise

  a $2x^2 - 4x - 6$ **Hint** $ac = -12$ **b** $3x^2 + 13x - 10$

                           $-6 + 2 = -4$

    $2x^2 - 6x + \text{..........} - 6$

  ....

3 Factorise

  a $3x^2 - 14x + 8$ **b** $4x^2 - 16x + 15$ **c** $8x^2 - 10x + 3$

  ....

4 Factorise

  a $9x^2 - 4$ **Hint** $9x^2 - 4$ is the difference   **b** $144x^2 - 49$
                   of two squares.
                   $(3x - \text{..........})(3x + \text{..........})$

  ....

Exam-style question

5 Factorise $6x^2 + 17x + 5$

                                            .... (2 marks)

Reflect

How can you tell that a factorisation will have negative numbers in it?

3 Simplifying expressions with brackets and powers

To expand a bracket, multiply every term inside the bracket by the term outside the bracket.

Guided practice

Worked exam question

Expand and simplify $x(x^2 + 2x + 5) - 3x + 1$

Expand the bracket.

$x(x^2 + 2x + 5) - 3x + 1$

$= x^3 + 2x^2 + \text{..........} - 3x + 1$

Collect like terms.

$= x^3 + 2x^2 + 2x + 1$

Multiply $\quad x\,(x^2 \quad + \quad 2x \quad + \quad 5)$

$= x \times x^2 + x \times 2x + x \times 5$

$= \quad x^3 \quad + \quad 2x^2 \quad + \quad 5x$

(1) Expand and simplify

a $4(a + 3b) + 2(a + b)$

b $5(x + 3y) + 4(2x - y)$

c $3(d - 2e) - (e + 3d)$

d $6(z - 2t) - 2(z - 3t)$

(2) Expand

a $x(x^2 + 3x + 4)$

b $x(x^2 - 2x + 1)$

c $a^2(a^2 + 2a - 3)$

d $y^3(4 - y^2 + 2y)$

(3) Expand and simplify

a $x(x^2 + 2x - 1) + 4x$

b $m(m^2 - 3m + 2) + 5m - 7$

c $x(x^2 - 3x + 5) + 4(x^2 - 3)$

d $y(y^2 + 5y - 2) - 7(y^2 - 2y + 3)$

(4) Expand and simplify

a $(x + 3)^2 - 2x$

b $(x - 4)^2 + 3x - 2$

Hint Square the bracket first.

c $(2a + 3)^2 + 4a$

d $(3p + 1)^2 - (2p + 3)$

(5) Expand

   a $x(x + 1)(x + 2)$

   b $y(y - 1)(y + 3)$

   Hint Expand the double brackets first.

   ....

   ....

(6) Expand and simplify

   a $y(y + 3)^2$

   b $x(x - 2)^2$

   ....

   ....

   c $a(a + 4)^2 - 3a$

   d $x(x + 1)^2 - (2x + 3)$

   ....

   ....

(7) Expand and simplify

   a $(x + 1)(x^2 + 2x + 3)$

   Hint $(x + 1)(x^2 + 2x + 3) = x(x^2 + 2x + 3) + 1(x^2 + 2x + 3)$

   ....

   b $(x - 2)(x^2 + x - 1)$

   c $(x + 4)(x^2 - 3x + 2)$

   ....

   ....

(8) Expand and simplify

   a $(x + 1)(x + 4)(x - 2)$

   $= (x + 1)(x^2 - \text{.........} + \text{.........})$

   Hint $(x + 1)\underbrace{(x + 4)(x - 2)}$

   Expand these first.

   ....

   b $(x + 2)(x - 3)(x + 1)$

   c $(y - 1)(y + 2)(y + 3)$

   ....

   ....

Exam-style question

(9) Expand and simplify $(x - 1)(x + 3)^2$

   .... (3 marks)

Reflect In Q8, does it matter which pair of brackets you expand first?

4 Simplifying expressions involving algebraic fractions

To simplify expressions with algebraic fractions:
- factorise the numerator and the denominator, if possible
- cancel common factors.

Guided practice

Simplify fully $\dfrac{3x + 3}{x^2 + 5x + 4}$

Factorise the numerator and the denominator.

$$\frac{3x + 3}{x^2 + 5x + 4} = \frac{3(\ldots\ldots + \ldots\ldots)}{(x + 4)(x + 1)}$$

$x^2 + 5x + 4 = (x + 4)(x + 1)$

Cancel common factors.

$$= \frac{3\cancel{(x + 1)}}{(x + 4)\cancel{(x + 1)}}$$

$$= \frac{3}{x + 4}$$

$\dfrac{(x + 1)}{(x + 1)} = 1$

(1) Simplify by cancelling the common factors.

a $\dfrac{6x^2y}{3xy^2}$ ....

b $\dfrac{2x^3}{y} \times \dfrac{xy^2}{4}$ ....

c $\dfrac{8}{x} \div \dfrac{4y}{x}$ ....

(2) Simplify

a $\dfrac{x}{2} + \dfrac{x}{6}$ ....

Hint $\overset{\times 3}{\frown}$

$\dfrac{x}{2} = \dfrac{3x}{6}$ $\dfrac{3x}{6} + \dfrac{x}{6} =$ ....

$\underset{\times 3}{\smile}$

b $\dfrac{x}{10} + \dfrac{x}{5}$ ....

c $\dfrac{3x}{4} + \dfrac{x}{3}$ ....

Hint

$\dfrac{\ldots\ldots}{12} + \dfrac{\ldots\ldots}{12} =$

(3) Simplify

a $\dfrac{x + 6}{2} - \dfrac{x}{4}$

$= \dfrac{2(x + 6)}{4} - \dfrac{x}{4}$ ....

Hint $\dfrac{x + 6}{2} = \dfrac{2(x + 6)}{4}$

Expand, then collect like terms.

b $\dfrac{x - 3}{4} + \dfrac{x + 5}{8}$ ....

(4) Simplify fully

a $\dfrac{x^2 + 2x}{x}$ ....

Hint Factorise then cancel.

b $\dfrac{x + 3}{x^2 - 9}$ ....

c $\dfrac{2(x + 4)}{x^2 + 5x + 4}$ ....

Exam-style question

(5) Simplify fully $\dfrac{x^2 + x - 2}{x^2 - 6x + 5}$

.... **(3 marks)**

Reflect How have you used common factors and common multiples in these questions?

Practise the methods

Answer this question to check where to start.

Check up

Tick the correct expansion of $(2x + 1)^2$

 A $\bigcirc$
$4x^2 + 1$

 B $\bigcirc$
$4x^2 + 4x + 1$

 C $\bigcirc$
$4x^2 + 2x + 1$

If you ticked B go to Q2.

If you ticked A or C go to Q1 for more practice.

1 Expand and simplify

a $(2x + 3)(2x + 1)$ **b** $(2x + 5)(2x + 5)$ **c** $(2x + 4)^2$

....

2 Expand and simplify

a $6(a - 2b) - 3(a + b)$ **b** $4x(x - 3) + 2(x - 5)$

....

3 Expand

a $x(x^2 + 3x - 4)$ **b** $y(y^2 - 2y + 5)$

....

4 Expand

a $x(x + 1)(x + 5)$ **b** $x(x - 3)(x + 2)$

....

5 Expand and simplify

a $(x - 2)(x - 3)(x + 4)$ **b** $(x - 5)(x + 1)^2$

....

6 Simplify

a $\dfrac{m}{3} - \dfrac{m}{5}$ ....   **b** $\dfrac{x}{6} + \dfrac{2x}{9}$ ....   **c** $\dfrac{5x}{7} + \dfrac{2x}{3}$ ....

7 Simplify fully

a $\dfrac{x^2 + 5x}{2x}$ ....   **b** $\dfrac{3x + 6}{x^2 - x - 6}$ ....

Exam-style question

8 Simplify

a $\dfrac{4x^2}{3y} \div \dfrac{2x}{y^3}$ .... (2 marks)

b $\dfrac{(2n + 1)^2}{4n^2 + 8n + 3}$ .... (2 marks)

Problem-solve!

① Show that the area of the rectangle is $6x^2 + x - 15$

$3x + 5$

$2x - 3$ ....

② Show that $(2x + 1)^2 - 2(x + 1)^2 \equiv 2x^2 - 1$

(3 marks)

③ Show that $(x + 2)^3$ can be written in the form $ax^3 + bx^2 + cx + d$ where a, b, c and d are integers.

.... (3 marks)

④ Expand

a $(x + 1)(x - 1)^2$

b $(x - 3)(x^2 - 25)$

....

....

⑤ Write an expression for the shaded area.
Simplify your answer as much as possible.

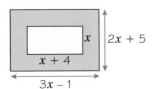

....

⑥ Write an expression for the volume of the cuboid.
Simplify your answer as much as possible.

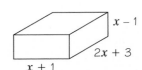

....

Exam-style questions

⑦ Simplify fully $\dfrac{x^2 - 4}{(x + 2)^2}$

.... (3 marks)

⑧ **a** Factorise $2x^2 + 7x + 3$ .... (2 marks)

b Simplify fully $\dfrac{2x^2 + 7x + 3}{x^2 - 9}$ .... (3 marks)

Now that you have completed this unit, how confident do you feel?

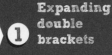
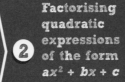
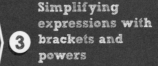
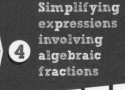

① Expanding double brackets

② Factorising quadratic expressions of the form $ax^2 + bx + c$

③ Simplifying expressions with brackets and powers

④ Simplifying expressions involving algebraic fractions

16   Unit 2 Manipulating algebra

③ Solving quadratic equations

This unit will help you to solve different types of quadratic equations.

AO1 Fluency check

① Factorise

a $x^2 + x - 12$

b $x^2 - 16$

c $2x^2 + 15x + 18$

② Expand

a $(x + 5)^2$

b $(x - 7)^2$

c $(x + 4)^2$

③ Write both solutions of

a $x + 2 = \pm 8$

b $x - 3 = \pm\sqrt{5}$

c $x + 1 = \pm\sqrt{2}$

④ **Number sense**

Tick the possible solutions of $a \times b = 0$

☐ $a = 0, b = 5$ ☐ $a = -4, b = 4$ ☐ $a = 7, b = 0$

☐ $a = 2, b = \frac{1}{2}$ ☐ $a = \sqrt{2}, b = 0$ ☐ $a = 0, b = 0$

Key points

You can solve some quadratic equations by factorising.

You can use the quadratic formula $x = \dfrac{-b \pm \sqrt{b^2 - 4ac}}{2a}$

to find the solutions to a quadratic equation of the form $ax^2 + bx + c = 0$

These **skills boosts** will help you to solve quadratic equations that you can factorise and those you cannot factorise.

① Solving quadratic equations by factorising

② Solving quadratic equations by completing the square

③ Solving quadratic equations by using the quadratic formula

You might have already done some work on solving quadratic equations. Before starting the first skills boost, rate your confidence with these questions.

① Solve $x^2 + x - 6 = 0$

② Solve $x^2 + 8x + 11 = 0$ by completing the square. Leave your answers in surd form.

③ Solve $x^2 + 3x - 5 = 0$ using the quadratic formula. Leave your answers in surd form.

 ow ident you?

1 Solving quadratic equations by factorising

To solve a quadratic equation like $x^2 - x - 6 = 0$, factorise.

Guided practice

Solve $x^2 - x - 6 = 0$

Factorise.
$$x^2 - x - 6 = 0$$

$(x + \text{..........})(x - \text{..........}) = 0$

So $x + \text{..........} = 0$ or $x - \text{..........} = 0$

$\qquad x = -2$ or $x = 3$

$a \times b = 0$ means that either $a = 0$ or $b = 0$

Check your answers.
When $x = -2$, $x^2 - x - 6 = 4 + 2 - 6 = 0$
When $x = 3$, $x^2 - x - 6 = 9 - 3 - 6 = 0$

① Solve

  a $x^2 + 2x - 8 = 0$

    $x = \text{..........}$ or $x = \text{..........}$

  b $x^2 - 2x - 15 = 0$

    $x = \text{..........}$ or $x = \text{..........}$

  c $x^2 + 9x + 14 = 0$

    $x = \text{..........}$ or $x = \text{..........}$

② Solve

  a $x^2 + 4x + 4 = 0$

    $x = \text{..........................}$

  b $x^2 - 6x + 9 = 0$

    $x = \text{..........................}$

  c $x^2 - 14x + 49 = 0$

    $x = \text{..........................}$

  d $x^2 - 16 = 0$

    $x = \text{..........................}$

  e $4x^2 - 100 = 0$

    $x = \text{..........................}$

  f $9x^2 - 144 = 0$

    $x = \text{..........................}$

Hint When both brackets are the same there are still two solutions.
You write $x = \text{..........}$ $x = \text{..........}$.

③ Solve

  a $x^2 - 8x = 0$

    $x = \text{..........}$ or $x = \text{..........}$

  b $x^2 + 3x = 0$

    $x = \text{..........}$ or $x = \text{..........}$

  c $2x^2 - 5x = 0$

    $x = \text{..........}$ or $x = \text{..........}$

Hint Factorise to $x(\text{..........} + \text{..........}) = 0$. One solution is $x = 0$

Exam-style question

④ Solve $y^2 + 3y - 28 = 0$

$\qquad\qquad\qquad\qquad\qquad y = \text{..........}$ or $y = \text{..........}$ **(2 marks)**

⑤ Solve

  a $x^2 - 3x = 4$

    $x = \text{..........}$ or $x = \text{..........}$

  b $x^2 - 3x = 10$

    $x = \text{..........}$ or $x = \text{..........}$

  c $x^2 = 4x + 21$

    $x = \text{..........}$ or $x = \text{..........}$

Hint Rearrange so the right-hand side $= 0$

Reflect   How many solutions does a quadratic equation have?

2 Solving quadratic equations by completing the square

Expressions like $(x + 2)^2$, $(x - 1)^2$ and $(x + 6)^2$ are called **perfect squares**. To 'complete the square', find the perfect square that gives the first two terms of the quadratic equation and add or subtract a number so that the expansion of the perfect square gives the original quadratic equation.

Guided practice

Worked exam question

Solve $x^2 + 4x + 1 = 0$

Write the perfect square that expands to $x^2 + 4x +$ a number.
$$(x + 2)^2 = x^2 + 4x + 4$$
What do you need to do to $x^2 + 4x + 4$ to get $x^2 + 4x + 1$?

$$(x + 2)^2 = x^2 + 4x + 4$$
$$(x + 2)^2 - 3 = x^2 + 4x + 1 \quad -3$$

Do the same to both sides.

Solve $(x + 2)^2 - 3 = 0$

$$(x + 2)^2 = \text{..........}$$
$$x + 2 = \pm\sqrt{\text{..............}}$$

Rearrange and square root both sides.

$$x + 2 = \sqrt{3} \qquad \text{or } x + 2 = -\sqrt{3}$$
$$x = -2 + \sqrt{3} \text{ or } x = -2 - \sqrt{3}$$

Give both solutions.

① Expand these perfect squares.
   a $(x + 1)^2$ **b** $(x - 1)^2$ **c** $(x + 3)^2$ **d** $(x - 2)^2$

   ....

② Write the perfect square that expands to
   a $x^2 + 2x +$ a number   **b** $x^2 - 2x +$ a number

   ....

③ Solve by completing the square.
   a $x^2 + 2x - 3 = 0$ **b** $x^2 - 2x - 4 = 0$ **c** $x^2 + 6x + 5 = 0$

   $x = $ .... or $x = $ .... $x = $ .... or $x = $ .... $x = $ .... or $x = $ ....

   d $x^2 - 4x - 2 = 0$ **e** $x^2 + 10x + 22 = 0$ **f** $x^2 - 8x + 14 = 0$

   $x = $ .... or $x = $ .... $x = $ .... or $x = $ .... $x = $ .... or $x = $ ....

Exam-style question

④ Solve $x^2 - 6x + 2 = 0$ by completing the square.
   Give your answers in surd form.

   $x = $ .... or $x = $ .... (3 marks)

Reflect   How does the coefficient of x in a quadratic expression help you choose the perfect square?

3 Solving quadratic equations by using the quadratic formula

When a question asks for the solutions to a quadratic equation to a number of decimal places (d.p.) or significant figures (s.f.), use the quadratic formula.

Guided practice

Solve $x^2 + 5x - 7 = 0$ Give your solutions to 2 d.p.

Compare the equation to $ax^2 + bx + c = 0$
Write down the values of a, b and c.

$a = 1 \quad b = 5 \quad c = $ ....

$x^2 + 5x \boxed{- 7} = 0$

$a = $ .... $\quad b = $ .... $\quad c = -7$

Substitute for a, b and c in the quadratic formula.

$$x = \frac{-b \pm \sqrt{b^2 - 4ac}}{2a}$$

$$x = \frac{-5 \pm \sqrt{5^2 - 4 \times 1 \times -7}}{2 \times 1} = \frac{-5 \pm \sqrt{\text{........} + 28}}{\text{........}}$$

$$x = \frac{-5 \pm \sqrt{\text{........}}}{\text{........}}$$

$x = -5 + \dfrac{\sqrt{\text{........}}}{2}$ gives one solution.

$x = -5 - \dfrac{\sqrt{\text{........}}}{2}$ gives the other solution.

Use your calculator.

$x = 1.14$ or $x = -6.14$

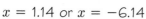

(1) Solve the quadratic equations. Give your solutions to 2 d.p.

a $x^2 + 3x + 1 = 0$

b $x^2 + 5x + 2 = 0$

c $x^2 - 7x + 11 = 0$

$x = $ .... or $x = $ ....

$x = $ .... or $x = $ ....

$x = $ .... or $x = $ ....

d $x^2 + 3x - 5 = 0$

e $x^2 - 5x - 4 = 0$

f $x^2 + 9x - 7 = 0$

$x = $ .... or $x = $ ....

$x = $ .... or $x = $ ....

$x = $ .... or $x = $ ....

(2) Solve the quadratic equations. Give your answers in surd form.

a $x^2 - x - 5 = 0$

b $x^2 + 7x + 4 = 0$

c $x^2 + 5x + 3 = 0$

$x = $ .... or $x = $ ....

$x = $ .... or $x = $ ....

$x = $ .... or $x = $ ....

Exam-style question

(3) Solve $x^2 - 3x + 1 = 0$. Give your solutions to 3 s.f.

$x = $ .... or $x = $ .... (3 marks)

Reflect Can you use the quadratic formula to solve quadratic equations that factorise?

Practise the methods

Answer this question to check where to start.

Check up

Tick the correct solution(s) to $x^2 + 4x - 12 = 0$

A ◯

$(x - 2)(x + 6)$
$x = -2$ or $x = 6$

B ◯

$(x + 2)^2 - 16 = 0$
$x + 2 = \pm 4$
$x = -6$ or $x = 2$

C ◯

$x = \dfrac{4 \pm \sqrt{16 + 48}}{2}$

If you ticked B go to Q4.

If you ticked A or C go to Q1 for more practice.

(1) Solve the quadratic equations by factorising.

a $x^2 - 9x + 18 = 0$

b $x^2 + 7x + 10 = 0$

c $x^2 + 3x - 10 = 0$

$x = \ldots\ldots$ or $x = \ldots\ldots$

$x = \ldots\ldots$ or $x = \ldots\ldots$

$x = \ldots\ldots$ or $x = \ldots\ldots$

(2) Solve the quadratic equations by completing the square.
Give your answers in surd form when necessary.

a $x^2 - 2x - 3 = 0$

b $x^2 + 8x + 6 = 0$

c $x^2 - 10x + 18 = 0$

$x = \ldots\ldots$ or $x = \ldots\ldots$

$x = \ldots\ldots$ or $x = \ldots\ldots$

$x = \ldots\ldots$ or $x = \ldots\ldots$

(3) Solve the quadratic equations by using the quadratic formula. Give your solutions to 2 d.p.

a $x^2 + 6x + 2 = 0$

b $x^2 - 8x + 5 = 0$

c $x^2 - 5x - 8 = 0$

$x = \ldots\ldots$ or $x = \ldots\ldots$

$x = \ldots\ldots$ or $x = \ldots\ldots$

$x = \ldots\ldots$ or $x = \ldots\ldots$

Exam-style questions

(4) Solve $x^2 + 4x - 11 = 0$
Give your answers to 2 d.p.

$x = \ldots\ldots$ or $x = \ldots\ldots$ **(3 marks)**

(5) Solve $x^2 - 2x - 5 = 0$
Give your answers in surd form.

$x = \ldots\ldots$ or $x = \ldots\ldots$ **(3 marks)**

Problem-solve!

(**1**) Write a quadratic equation that has the solutions $x = 2$ and $x = -5$

....

Exam-style question

(**2**) Solve $x^2 - 8x + 16 = 0$

$x =$ .... or $x =$ .... (3 marks)

(**3**) Solve $x^2 + 20x + 70 = 0$ by completing the square.
Give your answer to 3 s.f.

$x =$ .... or $x =$ ....

Exam-style questions

(**4**) The area of the rectangle is 44 cm².

Work out the dimensions of the rectangle.

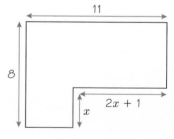

.... (3 marks)

(**5**) The area of this L-shape is 60 cm².
All lengths are given in centimetres.
Work out the length x.

.... (6 marks)

(**6**) Solve $3x^2 + 2x = 6$
Give your answers in surd form.

$x =$ .... or $x =$ .... (3 marks)

(**7**) Solve the quadratic equations. Give your answers in surd form.
   a $x^2 + 5x = 5$ **b** $x^2 + 2x = 4$ **c** $x^2 = 4x + 6$

$x =$ .... or $x =$ .... $x =$ .... or $x =$ .... $x =$ .... or $x =$ ....

Now that you have completed this unit, how confident do you feel?

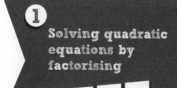

1 Solving quadratic equations by factorising

2 Solving quadratic equations by completing the square

3 Solving quadratic equations by using the quadratic formula

④ Algebraic graphs

This unit will help you to find the equations of parallel and perpendicular lines, to sketch quadratic graphs and to solve quadratic inequalities.

① Sketch the graphs of

  a $y = x^2$

  b $y = x^2 + 2$

② Write down the gradients of the lines with equations

  a $y = 3x - 2$ ....

  b $y = -\frac{1}{2}x + 6$ ....

  c $3x + 2y = 5$ ....

③ Solve by factorising.

  a $x^2 + 3x - 4 = 0$ ....

  b $x^2 + 5x - 14 = 0$ ....

④ Solve by completing the square. Give your answers to 1 decimal place (d.p.).

  a $x^2 + 4x + 3 = 0$ ....

  b $x^2 - 2x - 5 = 0$ ....

⑤ **Number sense**

  Write down the number halfway between

  a 1 and 7 ....

  b -3 and 5 ....

  c -5 and -1 ....

Key points

The equation of a straight line is $y = mx + c$ where m is the gradient and c is the y-intercept.	Parallel lines have the same gradient.	The x-values where a graph intersects the x-axis are the roots of the equation.

These **skills boosts** will help you to find the equations of parallel and perpendicular lines, to sketch quadratic graphs and to solve quadratic inequalities.

1 Equations of parallel and perpendicular lines	2 Using factorising to sketch quadratic graphs	3 Using completing the square to sketch quadratic graphs	4 Solving quadratic inequalities

You might have already done some work on algebraic graphs. Before starting the first skills boost, rate your confidence with these questions.

① Write down the equation of the line perpendicular to $y = 2x - 5$ that passes through (2, 0).

② Sketch the graph of $y = x^2 + 2x - 8$

③ Solve the inequality $x^2 + 2x > 8$

How confident are you?

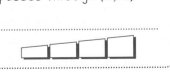

1 Equations of parallel and perpendicular lines

When a line has gradient m, lines parallel to it also have gradient m.
When a line has gradient m, lines perpendicular to it have gradient $-\frac{1}{m}$

Guided practice

Write down the equation of
a the line parallel to $y = 3x + 1$ that passes through (2, 10).
b the line perpendicular to $y = 3x + 1$ that passes through (3, −5).

a Find the gradient of the parallel line and substitute it into $y = mx + c$.
$$y = 3x + c$$

> All lines parallel to $y = 3x + 1$ have gradient 3.

Substitute the x and y-coordinates
(2, 10) into the equation and solve for c.
$$10 = 3 \times 2 + c$$
$$c = \text{...........}$$

> The coordinates of points on a line **satisfy** the equation of the line.

Equation is $y = 3x + 4$

b Use the gradient of the line $y = 3x + 1$ to find the gradient of the perpendicular.

$$-\frac{1}{3}$$

> Gradient of perpendicular $= -\frac{1}{m}$

Substitute the gradient into $y = mx + c$
$$y = -\frac{1}{3}x + c$$

Substitute the x and y-coordinates (3, −5) into the equation.
$$-5 = -\frac{1}{3} \times \text{...........} + c$$

$$c = \text{...........}$$
Equation is $y = -\frac{1}{3}x - 4$

① Write down the equation of the line parallel to
a $y = 2x - 3$ that passes through (3, 7).　　**b** $y = -x + 4$ that passes through (−1, −3).

$y = $ ....　　　　　　$y = $ ....

② Write down the equation of the line perpendicular to
a $y = 2x + 1$ that passes through (2, 2).　　**b** $y = -4x - 5$ that passes through (4, 2).

$y = $ ....　　　　　　$y = $ ....

③ Write down the equation of the line parallel to $3x + 2y = 7$
that passes through (2, 7).

> **Hint** Rearrange the equation into the form $y = mx + c$ to find the gradient.

$y = $ ....

Exam-style question

④ Write down the equation of the line perpendicular to $x + 5y = 8$ that passes through (1, 7).

$y = $ .... **(2 marks)**

Reflect

Draw diagrams to show why the perpendicular to a line with positive gradient has negative gradient, and vice versa.

2 Using factorising to sketch quadratic graphs

To sketch a quadratic graph you need to know its **roots**, **y-intercept**, the coordinates of the **turning point** and whether it is a maximum or a minimum. A quadratic graph has a vertical line of symmetry.

Guided practice

Worked exam question

Sketch the graph of $y = x^2 - x - 6$

Find the y-intercept by substituting $x = 0$ into $x^2 - x - 6 = 0$

$$y = 0^2 - 0 - 6 = \text{.............}$$

> At the y-intercept $x = 0$

Find the roots by solving $x^2 - x - 6 = 0$

> The roots are the solutions to $y = 0$

$$x^2 - x - 6 = 0$$
$$(x - 3)(x + 2) = 0$$

$x = \text{.............}$ or $x = \text{.............}$

Use symmetry to find the x-coordinate of the turning point.

$$\frac{x_1 + x_2}{2} = \frac{-2 + 3}{2} = \text{.............}$$

> Halfway between x_1 and $x_2 = \dfrac{x_1 + x_2}{2}$

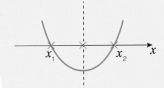

Substitute $x = \frac{1}{2}$ into $y = x^2 - x - 6$ to find the y-coordinate of the turning point.

$$y = \frac{1}{2}^2 - \frac{1}{2} - 6 = \text{.............}$$

Sketch the graph.

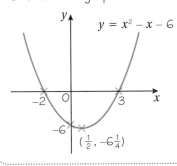

> Label the x and y-intercepts and give the coordinates of the turning point.

① Work out the coordinates of the turning point of each graph.

a

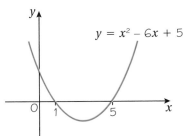

$y = x^2 - 6x + 5$

(............, ...)

b

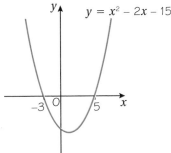

$y = x^2 - 2x - 15$

(............, ...)

② Work out the y-intercept of each graph in Q1.

a (0, ...)   **b** (0, ...)

③ Sketch the graph with roots $x = 2$ and $x = 6$, turning point $(4, -2)$ and y-intercept $(0, 10)$.

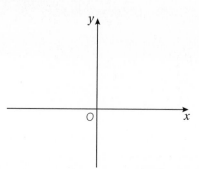

④ **a** Work out the y-intercept of the graph of $y = x^2 - 4x + 3$

y-intercept (.........., ...)

b Work out the roots of $y = x^2 - 4x + 3$

$x = $ .... and $x = $ ....

c Work out the turning point of $y = x^2 - 4x + 3$

d Sketch the graph of $y = x^2 - 4x + 3$

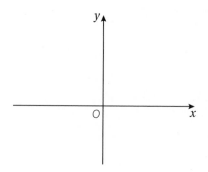

Exam-style questions

⑤ Sketch the graph of $y = x^2 - 6x + 8$

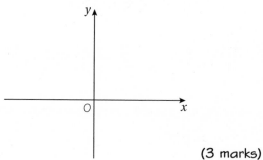

(3 marks)

⑥ Sketch the graph of $y = x^2 + 2x - 3$

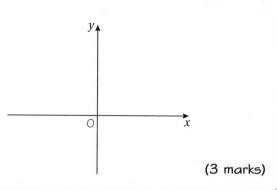

(3 marks)

Reflect How can you find the roots of a quadratic function that does not factorise?

3 Using completing the square to sketch quadratic graphs

For a quadratic function in completed square form, $a(x + b)^2 + c$, the turning point is $(-b, c)$.

Guided practice

Work out the roots and turning point of $y = x^2 + 6x + 8$

Complete the square.

$$(x + 3)^2 = x^2 + 6x + 9$$
$$\overset{-1}{\curvearrowright} (x + 3)^2 - 1 = x^2 + 6x + 8 \overset{-1}{\curvearrowleft}$$

Solve $(x + 3)^2 - 1 = 0$ to find the roots.

The roots are the solutions to $y = 0$

$$(x + 3)^2 = 1$$

$$(x + 3) = \text{..........}$$

$$x + 3 = \pm \text{..........}$$

Roots: $x = $ .... and $x = $ ....

Compare the completed square to
$$a(x + b)^2 + c$$
$$(x + 3)^2 \ominus 1$$

$a = $ ...., $b = $ ...., $c = $ ....

Turning point $= (-b, c) = (-3, -1)$

Halfway between
$-b - \sqrt{\text{.......}}$ and $-b + \sqrt{\text{.......}}$

(1) Work out the roots and turning point of $y = x^2 + 4x + 3$

Roots: $x = $ .... and $x = $ .... Turning point: (.........., ...)

(2) Work out the roots, turning point and y-intercept of $y = x^2 + 8x + 10$
Give your answers to 1 d.p.

Roots: $x = $ .... and $x = $ .... Turning point: (.........., ...) y-intercept: (.........., ...)

Exam-style question

(3) By completing the square, work out
the roots and sketch the graph
of $y = x^2 - 2x - 2$

.... (3 marks)

(4) By completing the square, work out the roots and turning point
of $y = -x^2 + 6x - 7$

Hint Take out -1 as a factor.
$$y = -1(x^2 - 6x + 7)$$
$$y = -1[(x - \text{..........})^2 + \text{..........}]$$
$$y = -(x - \text{..........})^2 - \text{..........}$$

Roots: $x = $ .... and $x = $ .... Turning point: (.........., ...)

Reflect Gina says, 'The x-coordinate of the turning point is halfway between the roots.
You can substitute to find the y-coordinate'. Try this method and see which you prefer.

4 Solving quadratic inequalities

To solve a quadratic inequality:
- rearrange so the right-hand side is 0
- find the roots of the quadratic function
- sketch the graph and test x-values from each section in the original inequality.

Guided practice

Worked exam question

Solve the inequality $x^2 + 3x - 4 > 6$

Rearrange to ... > 0
$$x^2 + 3x - 10 > 0$$

Subtract 6 from both sides.

Find the roots of $x^2 + 3x - 10 = 0$
$$(x - 2)(x + 5) = 0$$

Roots: $x = $ .... and $x = $ ....

Sketch the graph.
Test an x-value from each section in the original inequality.
$$x^2 + 3x - 4 > 6$$

① Test $x = -6$
$$(-6)^2 + (3 \times -6) - 4 = 14 > 6 \checkmark$$
So $x < -5$ is a solution.

② Test $x = 0$
$$0^2 + (3 \times 0) - 4 = -4 \not> 6$$
So $-5 < x < 2$ is not a solution.

③ Test $x = 3$
$$3^2 + (3 \times 3) - 4 = 14 > 6 \checkmark$$
So $x > 2$ is a solution.

The answer is $x < -5$ and $x > 2$

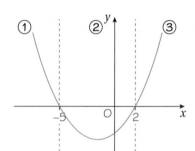

The graph divides the x-axis into three sections:
① $x < -5$, ② $-5 < x < 2$ and ③ $x > 2$

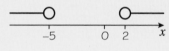

① Solve each inequality.

    a $x^2 + 2x - 3 < 0$

    b $x^2 - 5x + 4 > 0$

....

....

② Solve the inequality $x^2 - 4x - 5 \leqslant 0$

Hint At the roots, the inequality = 0, so include the roots in the solution to a $\geqslant$ or $\leqslant$ inequality.

....

Exam-style question

③ Solve $x^2 - 3x \geqslant 18$

.... (3 marks)

Reflect   Why is $x = 0$ always the easiest value to test?

Practise the methods

Answer this question to check where to start.

Check up

Tick the correct sketch graph for $x^2 - 2x - 8$

A 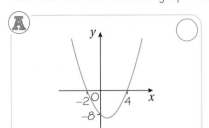 ◯

B 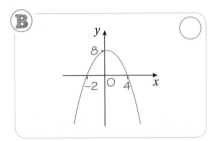 ◯

C 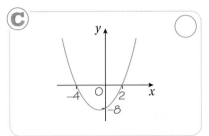 ◯

If you ticked A go to Q2.

If you ticked B or C go to Q1 for more practice.

(1) Write the roots and work out the y-intercept for the factorised quadratic equations.

a $x^2 - 5x + 6 = 0$
$(x - 3)(x - 2) = 0$

Roots: $x =$ .... and $x =$ ....

y-intercept: (............, ...)

b $x^2 + x - 12 = 0$
$(x + 4)(x - 3) = 0$

Roots: $x =$ .... and $x =$ ....

y-intercept: (............, ...)

(2) Write down the equation of the line parallel to $y = 4x + 1$ that passes through (0, 5).

$y =$ ....

Exam-style questions

(3) Write down the equation of the line parallel to $y = 2x$ that passes through (1, −3).

$y =$ .... (2 marks)

(4) **a** By factorising, work out the roots of $y = x^2 - 4x - 12$ .... (2 marks)

b Hence sketch the graph of $y = x^2 - 4x - 12$

Label the y-intercept and the turning point.

(2 marks)

(5) **a** Work out the roots of $y = x^2 - 4x - 3$ by completing the square. Give your answer to 1 d.p.

....

b Hence sketch the graph of $y = x^2 - 4x - 3$

Label the y-intercept and the turning point.

(6) Solve the inequality $x^2 - 2x - 3 < 0$

....

Problem-solve!

(1) **a** Write down the equation of line A.

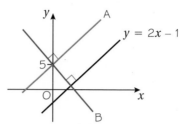

.... (2 marks)

b Write down the equation of line B.

.... (2 marks)

(2) ABC is a right-angled triangle.

The equation of line AC is $y = x + 2$ and A is the point (5, 7).

a Write down the equation of line AB.

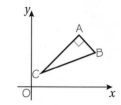

....

b Point B has x-coordinate 8.
Work out the y-coordinate of point B.

c C is the point (1, 3).
Write down the equation of line BC.

....

....

(3) Sketch the graph of $y = -x^2 - 5x - 6$

(4) Here is a sketch of $y = x^2 + bx + c$

The curve intersects the x-axis at the point A and (2, 0) and the
y-axis at (0, −2)

Work out the coordinate of the turning point of the graph.

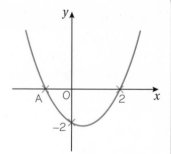

.... (4 marks)

(5) Solve $2x^2 - 7x - 4 > 0$

.... (3 marks)

Now that you have completed this unit, how confident do you feel?

1 Equations of parallel and perpendicular lines

2 Using factorising to sketch quadratic graphs

3 Using completing the square to sketch quadratic graphs

4 Solving quadratic inequalities

⑤ Sequences

This unit will help you to find missing terms in geometric and quadratic sequences.

AO1 Fluency check

① Write the first four terms in each sequence.

a First term 3, term-to-term rule 'add 4'. ....

b First term 20, term-to-term rule 'subtract 5'. ....

c First term 4, term-to-term rule 'multiply by 2'. ....

d First term 1000, term-to-term rule 'divide by 10'. ....

② Write the term-to-term rule for each sequence.

a 19, 26, 33, 40, … .... **b** 12, 9, 6, 3, … ....

③ Write the first four terms and the 10th term of the sequence with nth term

a $2n + 1$ .... **b** $3n - 8$ ....

④ Number sense

Complete the missing operations in the function machines.

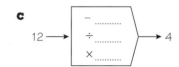

Key points

In an arithmetic sequence (also called an arithmetic progression), the term-to-term rule is 'add or subtract a constant number'.	In a geometric sequence, the term-to-term rule is 'multiply or divide by a constant number'.	To find the nth term of a quadratic sequence, find the 2nd difference.

To find the nth term of a quadratic sequence, find the 2nd difference.

```
                 2        8        18        32
1st difference        +6       +10       +14
2nd difference            +4        +4
```

These **skills boosts** will help you to identify a geometric sequence and find the term-to-term rule, and to find the nth term of quadratic and pattern sequences.

❶ **Continuing sequences** ❷ **Quadratic sequences** ❸ **Pattern sequences**

You might have already done some work on sequences. Before starting the first skills boost, rate your confidence using each method.

①
Write down the next three terms in the sequence.
96, 48, 24, 12, ...,
.........., ...

②
Label each sequence 'arithmetic' or 'geometric'.
a 1, 7, 13, 19, …, ...
b $\frac{1}{4}$, 1, 4, 16, …, ...
c 81, 27, 9, 3, …, ...

③
Work out the nth term of the quadratic sequence.
3, 9, 19, 33, …, ...

How confident are you?

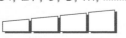

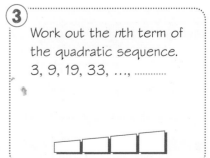

1 Continuing sequences

In an ascending sequence, the terms get larger; in a descending sequence, the terms get smaller.
A **finite** sequence has a fixed number of terms; an **infinite** sequence goes on forever.

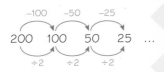 **Guided practice**

a Write the next three terms of the sequence: 200, 100, 50, 25, ...
State whether the sequence is arithmetic or geometric, and give the term-to-term rule.
b Write down the term-to-term rule for the sequence: 70, 98, 137.2, ...

a For a decreasing sequence try subtracting or dividing.

$$-100 \quad -50 \quad -25$$
200   100   50   25   ...
$$\div 2 \quad \div 2 \quad \div 2$$

> Subtraction is not the same each time.

> Division is the same each time.

Hint '...' means there are missing terms.

Continue the pattern.
$$\div 2 \quad \div 2 \quad \div 2$$
200, 100, 50, 25, 12.5, ..., 3.125

.... sequence; term-to-term rule is ....

> Division and multiplication give geometric sequences.

b 70, 98, 137.2, ...
Work out 2nd term ÷ 1st term.
$98 \div 70 = $ .... Check: $98 \times 1.4 = 137.2$ ✓
Term-to-term rule is ....

> Addition is not the same each time.

$70 \times$ .... $= 98$
so $98 \div 70 = $ ....

(1) Write the next three terms of each sequence.
State whether the sequence is arithmetic or geometric and give the term-to-term rule.

a 70, 60, 50, 40, ..., ..., ...

b 3, 6, 12, 24, ..., ..., ...

c 64, 16, 4, ..., ..., ...

d 7, −21, 63, ..., ..., ...

(2) Here are three sequences.
A 9, 3, −3, −9, −15   B $\frac{1}{25}, \frac{1}{5}, 1, 5, 25, ...$ C −0.5, 1, 2.5, 4, ..., 7, 8.5

Write the letter(s) of the sequence(s) that are

a ascending ....   **b** descending ....   **c** finite ....

d infinite ....   **e** arithmetic ....   **f** geometric. ....

(3) Work out the missing terms in each finite sequence.

a $\sqrt{2}$, 2, $2\sqrt{2}$, ..., ..., 8   **b** $4\sqrt{3}$, 12, ..., ..., $36\sqrt{3}$

Hint A multiplier doesn't have to be a whole number or a fraction.

Exam-style question

(4) a Write down the term-to-term rule of the sequence 500, 600, 720, ... **(1 mark)**
b The terms in the sequence are the amounts of money in a bank account after 1, 2, 3, ... years.
How much money will be in the account after 6 years? .... **(2 marks)**

Reflect   In Q4, could you work out the 6th term without writing down all the previous terms?

2 Quadratic sequences

The nth term of a quadratic sequence is $an^2 + bn + c$ where a, ~~b~~ and ~~c~~ are ... b or c, (or both), could be 0

$2a$ = 2nd difference $3a + b$ = 2nd term − 1st term $a + b + c$ = 1st term

Guided practice

Work out the nth term of the quadratic sequence.
6, 15, 28, 45, ...

Find the 1st and 2nd differences.

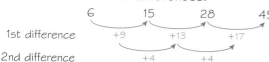

        6   15   28   45

1st difference   +9   +13   +17

2nd difference   +4   +4

$4 = 2a$
$a = \ldots\ldots$

> 2nd difference = $2a$

Use 2nd term − 1st term = $3a + b$
$$15 - 6 = 3 \times 2 + b$$
$$\ldots\ldots = 6 + b$$
$$b = \ldots\ldots$$

Use 1st term = $a + b + c$
$$6 = 2 + 3 + c$$
$$c = \ldots\ldots$$

Substitute a, b and c into $an^2 + bn + c$
nth term = $2n^2 + 3n + 1$

> Why?
> For 1st term, $n = 1$
> $an^2 + bn + c = a \times 1 + b \times 1 + c$
> $\qquad\qquad\quad = a + b + c$
> For 2nd term, $n = 2$
> $\quad an^2 + bn + c = 4a + 2b + c$
> So 2nd term − 1st term is
> $4a + 2b + c - (a + b + c) = 3a + b$

1. Work out the 1st differences. Follow the pattern to write the next three terms in each sequence.

   a 1   5   11   19, ..., ..., ...,
         +4   +6   ....
   b 2, 5, 10, 17, ..., ..., ...

   c 26, 24, 21, 17, ..., ..., ...
   d 42, 26, 13, 3, ..., ..., ...

2. Generate the first four terms of the sequence with nth term

   a $n^2 + 6$ ....
   b $2n^2 + n$ ....
   c $2n^2 - 5$ ....
   d $4n^2 - n + 1$ ....

   > **Hint**
   > Substitute $n = 1, 2, 3$ and 4 into the nth term.

3. Work out the nth term of each quadratic sequence.

   a 7, 20, 41, 70, ...
   b 5, 14, 27, 44, ...

4. Work out the nth term of each sequence. Hence find the 10th term.

   a 0, 1, 4, 9, ..., ...
   b 9, 15, 25, 39, ..., ...

   > **Hint**
   > Substitute $n = 10$

Exam-style question

5. Work out the nth term of the sequence 4, 12, 22, 34, ... **(3 marks)**

Reflect

For each sequence in Q2, check that the 2nd difference = $2a$.

You can find the *n*th term of a pattern sequence by
- looking at how the pattern grows
- writing it as a number sequence.

Guided practice

a Work out the *n*th term of the pattern sequence.

Pattern number   1   2   3   ...

b Hence write down the number of dots in the 10th pattern.

a Look for a relationship between the pattern number and the number of dots in the pattern.

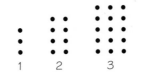

$1 + 2$ $2 + 2$ $...... + 2$ $n + ...$

Width = pattern number
Height = pattern number + 2

Write an expression for the number of dots in the *n*th rectangle.

$n(n + ...)$

b Substitute $n = 10$ into the *n*th term.

$10 × .... = ...$

① Here is the pattern sequence for triangular numbers.

Pattern number   1   2   3

This pattern sequence of rectangles is made from two sets of triangular numbers, one red and one black.

Pattern number   1   2   3

a Work out the *n*th term of the numbers of dots in the pattern sequence of rectangles.

....

b Hence write down the *n*th term of the numbers of dots in the pattern sequence of triangular numbers.

....

Hint Each triangular number is half the rectangular number.

② This sequence is the numbers of dots in the pattern sequence for triangular numbers in Q1.

1, 3, 6, 10, 15, ...

Work out the *n*th term of the number sequence by using 1st and 2nd differences.

....

Reflect   Are your answers to Q1b and Q2 equivalent?

Practise the methods

Answer this question to check where to start.

Check up

Tick the correct method to find the nth term of the sequence   0, 4, 12, 24, 40, …

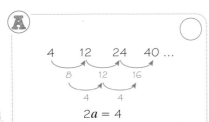

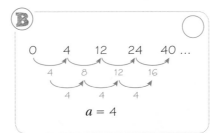

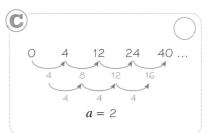

If you ticked C go to Q3.

If you ticked A go to Q2.

If you ticked B go to Q1.

(1) **a** Write down the first four terms of the sequence with general term

    i n^2 ....   **ii** $2n^2$ ....

    iii $3n^2$ ....   **iv** $4n^2$ ....

b For each sequence, work out the 1st and 2nd differences. Describe the relationship between the 2nd difference and the number in front of n^2 in the general term.

....

(2) Work out the nth term of each sequence.

    a 4, 12, 24, 40, … , ...   **b** 0, 4, 12, 24, 40, … , ...

    c Can you ignore a zero term in a sequence? ....

Exam-style questions

(3) **a** Draw the next pattern in the sequence.

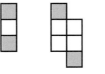

                                                                      (1 mark)

b Write the nth term of the sequence of numbers of white squares. .... (1 mark)

c Hence work out the nth term of the sequence of numbers of black and white squares.

                                                                  .... (1 mark)

(4) **a** Write down the term-to-term rule for the sequence   200, 300, 450, 675, … ,

                                                      .... (1 mark)

b Work out the 8th term in the sequence.

                                                      .... (2 marks)

Problem-solve!

(1) Write down the missing terms in each sequence.

   a 144, 48, ..., ..., 1.$\dot{7}$ **b** 17, 27.2, ..., ..., 111.4112

Exam-style question

(2) Jack has forgotten his four-digit PIN. He knows it includes a 2 and a 4, and that the numbers in the correct order form a sequence.

Write two possible four-digit numbers that could be Jack's PIN. .... **(2 marks)**

(3) Decide whether each sequence is finite or infinite.

   a Positive multiples of 2, less than 50   ....

   b Multiples of 7, less than or equal to 49   ....

Exam-style questions

(4) Work out the missing terms in the sequence.

$$3, \ldots, \ldots, \frac{1}{\sqrt{3}}, \frac{1}{3}$$ ...., ... **(2 marks)**

(5) The value of a car depreciates by a fixed percentage each year.

The table shows its value, to the nearest £, for three consecutive years.

Year	2014	2015	2016
Value	£16 500	£13 530	£11 095

Calculate the predicted value of the car in 2018, to the nearest £10.   .... **(3 marks)**

(6) Here are the first four terms of a quadratic sequence.

   3, 12, 27, 48, ...

Work out the first term greater than 200.   .... **(4 marks)**

(7) A supermarket stacks cans of dog food.

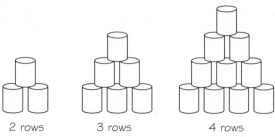

  2 rows   3 rows   4 rows

Write down the number of cans in a stack n rows high.   .... **(3 marks)**

Now that you have completed this unit, how confident do you feel?

1 Continuing sequences   **2** Quadratic sequences   **3** Pattern sequences

⑥ Congruence and similarity

This unit will help you to find missing lengths and angles in congruent and similar shapes.

AO1 Fluency check

① Work out the scale factor of each enlargement.

a
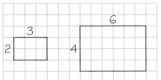

b
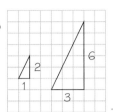

② Write down the sizes of the angles marked with letters. Give reasons for your answers.

a

b

c

③ Number sense

Use the given number facts to help you to complete the calculations.

a

$5 \times 1.2 = 6$

$6 \div 1.2 = \text{............}$ $6 \div 5 = \text{............}$

b

$8 \times 2.5 = 20$

$20 \div 2.5 = \text{............}$ $20 \div 8 = \text{............}$

Key points

Congruent shapes are identical. Their angles are the same size and corresponding sides are the same length.

Two shapes are similar when one is an enlargement of the other. Corresponding angles are equal. Corresponding sides are enlarged by the same scale factor.

These **skills boosts** will help you to prove that shapes are congruent or similar, and to use congruence and similarity to find missing lengths and angles.

| 1 Deciding if shapes are congruent or similar | 2 Proving that triangles are similar | 3 Perimeters and areas of enlargement | 4 Similar shapes |

You might have already done some work on congruence and similarity. Before starting the first skills boost, rate your confidence using each method.

① Which triangles are congruent?

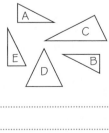

② Prove that triangles ABE and ACD are similar.

③ A square of side 5 cm is enlarged by scale factor 2. Work out the area of the enlarged shape.

④ Work out length DC.

How confident are you?

1 Deciding if shapes are congruent or similar

Two triangles are congruent when one (or more) of these conditions is true:
- SSS (all three sides equal)
- SAS (two sides and the included angle are equal)
- AAS or ASA or SAA (two angles and a corresponding side are equal)
- RHS (right angle, hypotenuse and one other side are equal).

Guided practice

a Which triangle is congruent to A?
b Which triangle is similar to A?

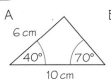
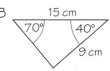
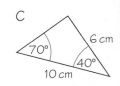

---

a For congruence, look for a triangle with the same side lengths that translates, rotates or reflects to fit exactly on to A.

.... is congruent to A.
Write one or more reasons.
    ASA or SAS

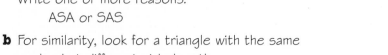

b For similarity, look for a triangle with the same angles but different side lengths.

Sketch the triangles with matching angles in the same position. Colour corresponding sides.

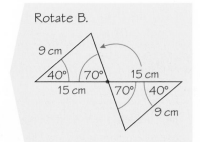

Rotate B.

Find the scale factor for one pair of corresponding sides.

$6 \times$ scale factor $= 9 \Rightarrow$ scale factor $\dfrac{9}{......} = \dfrac{......}{2} = 1.5$

Check this scale factor works for the other corresponding sides.
    $10 \times 1.5 = 15$ ✓

.... is similar to A.

---

① Show that the triangles in each pair are congruent. State the reason.

a

b

c

d

Exam-style question

(2) Show that

A

B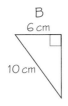

C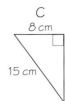

a A and B are similar

.... (2 marks)

b B and C are *not* similar.

.... (2 marks)

(3) These two triangles are congruent.
Work out the lengths and angles labelled with letters.

Hint Sketch the shapes with matching sides and angles in the same position.

  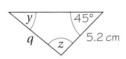

....

Exam-style questions

(4) Triangle ABC is mathematically similar to triangle DEF. Work out the lengths of:

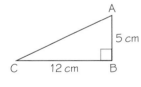 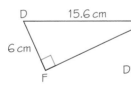

Diagram NOT accurately drawn

a FE .... (2 marks)

b AC. .... (2 marks)

(5) Here are two congruent triangles.

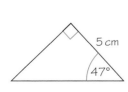 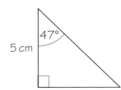

Choose from one of the reasons to say why these triangles are congruent.

SSS   SAS   ASA   RHS

.... (1 mark)

Reflect   How does sketching shapes with matching angles in the same position help you to identify corresponding sides?

2 Proving that triangles are similar

To prove that two shapes are similar:
* show that their corresponding angles are equal *or* show that all sides are enlarged by the same scale factor.

Guided practice

Prove that triangles ABC and
ADE are similar.

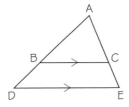

_____

On the diagram, label equal angles with
the same letter.

Write a reason for the equal angles.

∠ABC = ∠ADE = x corresponding angles

∠ACB = ∠AED = y .... angles

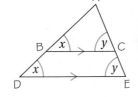

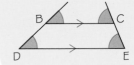

BC and DE are parallel.

Draw the two triangles separately and label equal angles.

∠BAC and ∠DAE are the same angle.

Triangles ABC and ADE are similar

because they have .... angles.

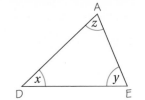

① Prove that triangles VWX and VYZ are similar.

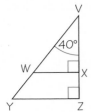

Hint Find all the
angles. Give a reason
for the equal angles.

....

....

② Prove that triangles MNR and PQR are similar.

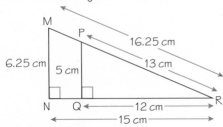

Hint Show that all the
sides are enlarged by
the same scale factor.

....

....

Exam-style question

③ Prove that triangles STU and VUW are similar.

Diagram NOT
accurately drawn

....

....

(2 marks)

Reflect

Which angle facts in parallel lines have you used to prove that triangles are similar?

3 Perimeters and areas of enlargement

When a shape is enlarged by a scale factor
- its perimeter is enlarged by the same scale factor
- its area is enlarged by the (scale factor)^2.

Guided practice

This rectangle is enlarged by a scale factor of 3.
Work out:
a the perimeter of the enlargement
b the area of the enlargement.

2 cm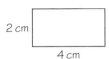
4 cm

a Work out the perimeter of the rectangle.

Perimeter of rectangle = 2 + 4 + ... + ...

= ....cm

Multiply the perimeter by the scale factor.

Perimeter of enlargement = 3 × .... = ...cm

b Work out the area of the rectangle.

Area of rectangle = 2 × .... = ...cm^2

Multiply the area by the (scale factor)^2.

Area of enlargement = 3^2 × ....

= 9 × .... = ...cm^2

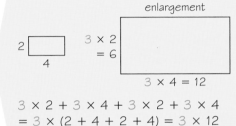

enlargement

2 ▢ 3 × 2 = 6
4

3 × 2 = 6   3 × 4 = 12

3 × 2 + 3 × 4 + 3 × 2 + 3 × 4
= 3 × (2 + 4 + 2 + 4) = 3 × 12

2 | 2 × 4 = 8 | 3 × 2 = 6 | 6 × 12 = 72
4

3 × 4 = 12

3 × 2 × 3 × 4 = 3^2 × 2 × 4
= 3^2 × 8

① a Draw the enlargement of the rectangle by scale factor 2.
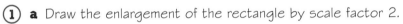

b Work out the perimeter of the rectangle and the perimeter of the enlargement.

3
1

....

② This square is enlarged by scale factor 4. Work out

a the perimeter of the enlargement ....

b the area of the enlargement. ....

2 cm

③ The two triangles, A and B, are mathematically similar.

a Work out the scale factor of the enlargement from A to B. ....

b The area of triangle A is 7 cm^2. Work out the area of triangle B. ....

B
A

2 cm   5 cm

Exam-style question

④ These two triangles are mathematically similar.

X

5 cm
←—8 cm—→

Y
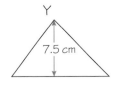
7.5 cm

Diagram NOT accurately drawn

Work out the area of triangle Y.   .... (2 marks)

Reflect

When you double the lengths of the sides of a shape, do you double its area?

4 Similar shapes

To find a length on the enlargement, *multiply* by the scale factor.

To find a length on the original, *divide* by the scale factor.

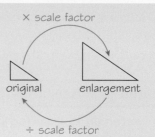

× scale factor

original   enlargement

÷ scale factor

Guided practice

Work out the length of DE.

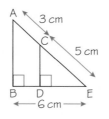

Show that triangles ABE and CDE are similar.

∠AEB = ∠ ....   same angle

∠ABE = ∠CDE = ...°   given

∠EAB = ∠ECD   .... angles

Triangles ABE and CDE are similar because they have .... angles.

Draw the two triangles separately.

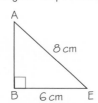

Find the scale factor of the enlargement for CDE to ABE.

5 × scale factor = 8

Scale factor = $\frac{..........}{5}$ = ...

Divide by the scale factor to find lengths on CDE.

DE = ... ÷ 1.6 = ... cm

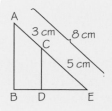

AB and CD are parallel, because ∠ABE and ∠CDE are corresponding angles.

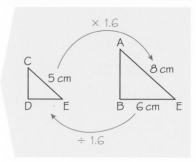

① **a** Show that triangles PQT and PRS are similar.

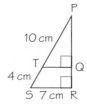

b Work out the length of TQ.   ....

(2) **a** Show that triangles ABC and CDE are similar.

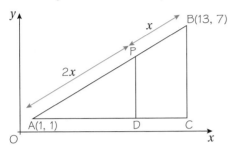

b Work out the length of BC.

....

(3) The diagram shows that point P divides the line AB in the ratio 2 : 1.

a Work out the lengths AC and BC and write them on the diagram.

b Draw triangles APD and ABC separately.

Work out the scale factor that enlarges APD to ABC.

Hint $2x \times$ scale factor $= 3x$

....

c Use the scale factor to work out the lengths PD and AD.

....

d Hence write down the coordinates of P.

....

Exam-style questions

(4)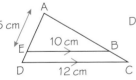

Diagram NOT accurately drawn

a Work out the length AD. .... (2 marks)

b Work out the length DE. .... (2 marks)

(5) Triangles ABD and ECD are mathematically similar.

Write a fraction using two sides that is

equivalent to $\dfrac{CD}{BD}$

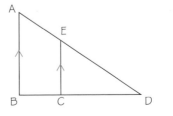

.... (1 mark)

Reflect How does drawing the triangles separately help you to find the scale factor?

Practise the methods

Answer this question to check where to start.

Check up

Triangle ABC is mathematically similar to triangle FDE.
Tick the correct calculation to find length BC.

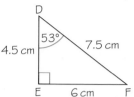

A 4.5 ÷ 1.5 ○   **B** 6 ÷ 1.5 ○   **C** 4.5 × 1.5 ○

If you ticked A go to Q2.   If you ticked B or C go to Q1.

1 Triangles GHI and JKL are similar.
  a Work out the missing angles indicated.
  b Sketch the triangles with matching angles in the same position.
  c Work out the missing lengths.

  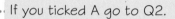

2 Show that triangles MNO and PRQ are congruent.

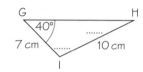

Exam-style question

3 Prove that triangles RSU and VTU are mathematically similar.

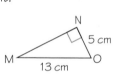 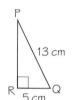

Diagram NOT accurately drawn

(3 marks)

4 These two triangles are mathematically similar.
Triangle A has an area of 9 cm².
Work out the area of triangle B.

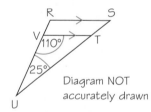

5 **a** Work out angle VWX.
  b Show that triangles VWX and XYZ are similar.
  c Work out length XY.

 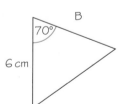 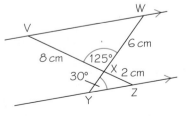

Problem-solve!

(1) Show that triangles
ABC and CDE are
congruent.

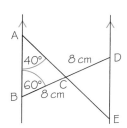

Diagram NOT
accurately drawn

(4 marks)

(2) These two trapezia are similar.
Work out the angles and lengths labelled
with letters.

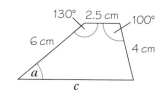
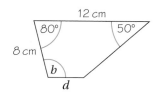

....

(3) An irregular pentagon has area 100 cm².
Its sides are enlarged by a scale factor of 3.
Work out the area of the enlargement.

.... (2 marks)

(4) The area of triangle ADE is 80 cm².
Work out the area of triangle ABC.

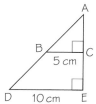

Diagram NOT
accurately drawn

.... (4 marks)

(5) Here is a 1 cm cube.

a The cube is enlarged by scale factor 2.
Sketch the enlargement. Label the lengths of its sides.

b Calculate the volumes of the 1 cm cube and the enlarged cube. ....

c Complete the statement.
When the cube is enlarged by scale factor 2, its volume is enlarged by scale factor 2^......... .

(6) **a** Explain why these two spheres are mathematically similar.   A   B

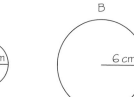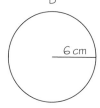

....

....

b The volume of sphere A is 33.5 cm³.
Work out the volume of sphere B to 1 d.p.

....

Now that you have completed this unit, how confident do you feel?

1 Deciding if shapes
are congruent or
similar

2 Proving that
triangles are
similar

3 Perimeters
and areas of
enlargement

4 Similar
shapes

(7) Right-angled triangles

This unit will help you to find lengths and angles in right-angled triangles.

A01 Fluency check

(1) Use a calculator to work out the values. Give your answers to 3 decimal places (d.p.).

   a $\sin 40°$ ....   **b** $\tan 45°$ ....   **c** $\cos 80°$ ....   **d** $\tan 70°$ ....

(2) Use a calculator to work out the sizes of the angles. Give your answers to 1 d.p.

   a $\sin^{-1}(0.2)$ ....   **b** $\cos^{-1}(0.8)$ ....   **c** $\sin^{-1}(0.56)$ ....   **d** $\tan^{-1}(3)$ ....

(3) Solve for x.

   a $\dfrac{x}{5} = 12$ ....   **b** $\dfrac{5}{x} = 10$ ....   **c** $\dfrac{8}{x} = 12$ ....

(4) Use Pythagoras' theorem to calculate the lengths labelled with letters. Give your answers to 1 d.p.

   a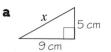

   b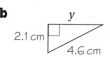

Key points

In a right-angled triangle:

$$\sin x = \frac{O}{H} \qquad \cos x = \frac{A}{H}$$

$$\tan x = \frac{O}{A}$$

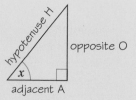

SOHCAHTOA can help you remember these trigonometric ratios.

These **skills boosts** will help you to find missing lengths and angles by using trigonometry and Pythagoras' theorem.

1 Finding lengths in right-angled triangles   **2** Finding angles in right-angled triangles   **3** Using trigonometry to solve problems   **4** Using Pythagoras' theorem in 3D problems

You might have already done some work on right-angled triangles. Before starting the first skills boost, rate your confidence using each method.

1 Calculate the length x, correct to 1 d.p.
  (triangle with 50°, 6 cm)

2 Calculate the angle y, correct to 1 d.p.
  (triangle with 4 cm, 9 cm)

3 Calculate the length z, correct to 1 d.p.
  (triangle with 10 cm, 25°)

4 Calculate the length d, correct to 1 d.p.
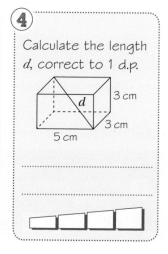
  (cuboid with 3 cm, 3 cm, 5 cm)

How confident are you?

1 Finding lengths in right-angled triangles

You can use the sin, cos and tan ratios to find missing lengths.

Guided practice

Calculate the length x, correct to 1 d.p.

6 cm
28°
x

Worked exam question

Label O (opposite), A (adjacent) and H (hypotenuse).
Write what you know and what you want to find.
Write down the ratio that uses these sides.

$$\cos = \frac{A}{\text{........}}$$

Substitute the angle and sides.

$$\cos 28° = \frac{x}{6}$$
$$6 \cos 28° = x$$

$x =$ .... = ...cm (to 1 d.p.)

6 cm H
28°   O
x A

know H   want A

SOH CAH TOA

Solve for x.

Round to 1 d.p.

① Calculate the length x, correct to 1 d.p.

a
8 cm
32°
x
....

b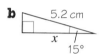
5.2 cm
x
15°
....

② Calculate the length y, correct to 1 d.p.

a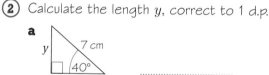
y 7 cm
40°
....

b
y
53°
8.5 cm
....

③ Calculate the length z, correct to 1 d.p.

a
58° 4.2 cm
z
....

b
35° 10 cm
z
....

④ Calculate the length marked with a letter in each triangle. Give your answers to 1 d.p.

a
7 cm
m
30°
....

b
n 5 cm
48°
....

c
p
70°   12 cm
....

Exam-style question

⑤ A ladder 5 m long is placed against a wall.
The ladder makes an angle of 65° with the ground.

Calculate the distance from the base of the wall to the ladder.
Give your answer to the nearest centimetre.

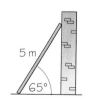

Diagram NOT accurately drawn

5 m
65°

.... (3 marks)

Reflect

How have you used equation-solving methods to work out lengths?

2 Finding angles in right-angled triangles

The inverse operation of sin is $\sin^{-1}$
cos is $\cos^{-1}$
tan is $\tan^{-1}$

Guided practice

Calculate the angle w. Give your answer to 1 d.p.

_____

Label O (opposite), A (adjacent) and H (hypotenuse).
Write the sides you know and the ratio that uses them.

O, H .... = ⎯⎯⎯⎯⎯

SOH CAHTOA

Substitute the angle and sides.

$\sin w = \dfrac{5}{\text{.........}}$

Use $\sin^{-1}$.

$\sin^{-1}(\sin w) = \sin^{-1}\left(\dfrac{5}{\text{.........}}\right)$

$w = $ _____° (to 1 d.p.)

Worked exam question

Do the same to both sides.
$\sin^{-1}(\sin w) = w$

① Calculate the angle m. Give your answers to 1 d.p.

a 7 cm ◁ m ◁ 3 cm

....

b 5 cm ◁ m ◁ 9 cm

....

② Calculate the angles marked with letters. Give your answers to the nearest degree.

a 5 cm, t, 7 cm

....

b 11 m, s, 4.8 m

....

③ The diagram shows an aeroplane starting its descent.

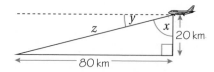

a Calculate angle x, to the nearest degree. ....

b Work out the angle of **depression**, y. ....

Exam-style question

④ A bird flies in a straight line from the ground
to the top of a post 6 m tall.
Calculate the angle of **elevation**, to 1 d.p.

Hint
Angle of elevation

horizontal

6 m Diagram NOT accurately drawn
15 m

.... (3 marks)

Reflect

How have you used equation-solving methods to work out angles?

3 Using trigonometry to solve problems

Guided practice

Calculate the length x, correct to 1 d.p.

Label O (opposite), A (adjacent) and H (hypotenuse).
Write down the side you want and the side you know.

want .... know ....

$$\sin = \frac{O}{H}$$

$\boxed{\text{SOH}}$CAHTOA

$$\sin \ldots\ldots\ldots = \frac{7}{x}$$

$$x \sin 50° = 7$$

$$x = \frac{7}{\sin 50°}$$

Solve for x.

$$x = \ldots\ldots\ldots \text{ cm (to 1 d.p.)}$$

① Calculate the length y, correct to 1 d.p.

a

b

c

d

....

② A ladder makes an angle of 15° with a wall.
It reaches 4.8 m up the wall.

Hint Use trigonometry
or Pythagoras' theorem.

a Work out the length of the ladder,
correct to the nearest metre.

....

b Work out the distance from the base of
the ladder to the wall, correct to 1 d.p.

....

③ Manish builds a ramp up a step.
The step is 15 cm high.
The ramp is at an angle of 18° to the ground.
Calculate the length of wood needed to make the ramp, to the
nearest centimetre.

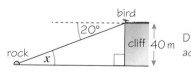

....

Exam-style question

④ A cliff is 40 m high. A bird
flies from the top of the cliff
to a rock, at an angle of
depression of 20°.

a Write down angle x.

.... **(2 marks)**

b Work out the distance from the rock to the base of the cliff.
Give your answers to a suitable degree of accuracy.

.... **(2 marks)**

Reflect In Q2, was it easier to use trigonometry or Pythagoras' theorem in part b?

4 Using Pythagoras' theorem in 3D problems

You can use Pythagoras' theorem to find lengths in 3D solids.

Guided practice

Work out d, the length of the diagonal AH of the cuboid.
Give your answer to 1 d.p.

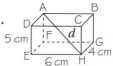

Sketch the triangles AFH and EFH.
Use Pythagoras' theorem to find FH.

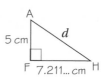

You need FH to find d.

$FH^2 = 4^2 + 6^2$

$FH = \sqrt{} = 7.211... \text{ cm}$

Use FH and AF to find d.

$d^2 = 5^2 + 7.211...^2$

$d = \sqrt{} = = 8.8 \text{ cm (to 1 d.p.)}$

1. JKLMNPQR is a cuboid.

   a Work out the length of PR, the diagonal of the base.

   b Sketch the triangle KPR.

   c Work out the length of KR, the diagonal of the cuboid.

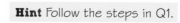

2. Work out the length of QW, the diagonal of the cuboid.

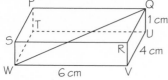

   Hint Follow the steps in Q1.

3. Calculate the length of the diagonal of a 3 cm cube.
   Give your answer to 1 d.p.

   Hint Sketch the cube and its diagonal.

4. Pyramid ABCDE has a rectangular base.
   Calculate the length of the diagonal EC.

Exam-style question

5. The diagram shows the dimensions of an ice cream cone.
   Work out h, the height of the cone.
   Give your answer to the nearest millimetre.

(3 marks)

Reflect

In a right-angled triangle, when do you use Pythagoras' theorem to work out a length, and when do you use trigonometry?

Practise the methods

Answer this question to check where to start.

Check up

Which method for calculating the length x is *not* correct?

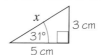

A $\quad x = \sqrt{3^2 + 5^2}$

B $\quad x = \dfrac{3}{\sin 31°}$

C $\quad x = 5 \cos 31°$

D $\quad x = \dfrac{3}{\cos 59°}$

If you ticked C go to Q2.   If you ticked A, B or D go to Q1.

1 a Complete these statements for the triangle.

i $y^2 = 10^2 +$ ....

$y = \sqrt{.............. + ...}$

ii $\sin 55° = \dfrac{..............}{y}$

$y = \dfrac{..............}{\sin 55°}$

iii $\cos 55° = \dfrac{..............}{y}$

$y = \dfrac{..............}{\cos 55°}$

b Use parts **a**, **i**, **ii** or **iii** to find the length y, to 1 d.p.   ....

2 Calculate the lengths and angles marked with letters. Give your answers to 1 d.p.

a 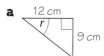   **b**    **c**    **d**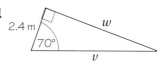

....

....

Exam-style questions

3 A surveyor stands 50 m from a building and measures an angle of elevation of 30° to the top of the building.

 Diagram NOT accurately drawn

Calculate the height of the building, to 3 significant figures.   .... (3 marks)

4 Work out the length of the diagonal of the 10 cm cube.

.... (3 marks)

Problem-solve!

(1) A radio mast 20 m tall is held in position
by steel cables 24 m long.

Calculate the angle the steel cables make with the ground.
Give your answer to 1 d.p.

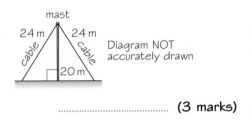

Diagram NOT
accurately drawn

.... **(3 marks)**

(2) Lucy sails 7 km west and then 4 km north.

a Calculate the **bearing** she needs to sail on
to return to her starting position.

b Work out the shortest distance to the starting position.
Give your answer to 2 d.p.

....

....

(3) Jim stands at the top of an 18 m lighthouse
and sees a boat and a rock in the sea below.

The angle of depression to the rock is 65°.
The angle of depression to the boat is 42°.
Work out the distance between the boat and the rock.
Give your answer to the nearest metre.

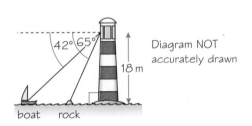

Diagram NOT
accurately drawn

.... **(3 marks)**

(4) A box is in the shape of a cuboid 5 cm by 4 cm by 20 cm.
Will a pencil of length 25 cm fit into the box?

Show your working.

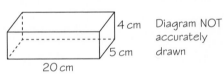
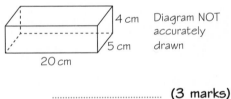

Diagram NOT
accurately
drawn

.... **(3 marks)**

(5) ABC is an equilateral triangle of side 2 cm.
AD is the perpendicular bisector of CB.

a Label the sizes of all the angles on the diagram.

b Work out the length AD. Give your answer in surd form.

c From the diagram find

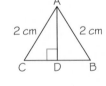

....

i cos 60° .... **ii** sin 60° .... **iii** cos 30° .... **iv** sin 30° ....

Leave your answers in surd form where appropriate.

Now that you have completed this unit, how confident do you feel?

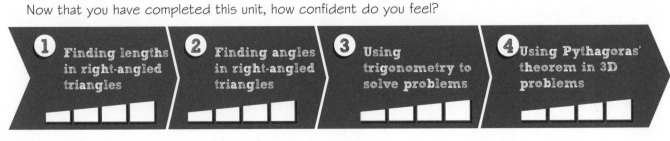

① Finding lengths in right-angled triangles

② Finding angles in right-angled triangles

③ Using trigonometry to solve problems

④ Using Pythagoras' theorem in 3D problems

Trigonometry in non-right-angled triangles

This unit will help you find lengths, angles and areas in triangles without right angles.

AO1 Fluency check

(1) Sketch a triangle. Label its vertices A, B and C.
Label the side opposite $\angle A$ with letter a.
Label the side opposite $\angle B$ with letter b.
Label the side opposite $\angle C$ with letter c.

(2) Solve

   a $\dfrac{5}{7} = \dfrac{c}{2}$ ....

   b $\dfrac{3}{8} = \dfrac{d}{4}$ ....

   c $9 = \dfrac{1}{2} \times e \times 6$ ....

(3) Calculate the angles, to 1 decimal place (d.p.).

   a $\sin w = \dfrac{12}{14}$ ....
   b $\sin x = \dfrac{3}{8}$ ....
   c $\cos y = \dfrac{5}{7}$ ....
   d $\cos z = \dfrac{2}{9}$ ....

(4) Number sense

   a Here are two equivalent fractions: $\dfrac{2}{3} = \dfrac{4}{6}$

     Are their reciprocals also equivalent? ....

   b Does this work for other equivalent fractions? ....

Key points
↓

In a triangle ABC:

- cosine rule: $a^2 = b^2 + c^2 - 2bc\cos A$
- sine rule: $\dfrac{a}{\sin A} = \dfrac{b}{\sin B} = \dfrac{c}{\sin C}$
- area $= \frac{1}{2}ab\sin C$

These **skills boosts** will help you to find missing lengths and angles, and calculate the area of triangles.

1 Finding lengths using the sine rule

2 Using the cosine rule and the area formula

3 Using the sine and cosine rules to find angles

4 Using area $= \frac{1}{2}ab\sin C$ to solve problems

You might have already done some work on lengths, angles and areas in triangles without right angles.
Before starting the first skills boost, rate your confidence using each method.

(1) Calculate the length m, correct to 1 d.p.

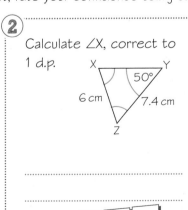

(2) Calculate $\angle X$, correct to 1 d.p.

(3) Calculate the area of triangle PQR, correct to 1 d.p.

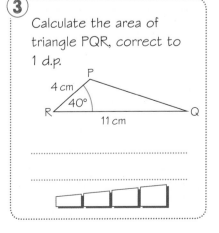

Skills boost

1 Finding lengths using the sine rule

Use the sine rule when you know two angles and a non-included side.

 or

Guided practice

Calculate the length PQ, correct to 1 d.p.

Label the triangle ABC and the sides a, b and c.

Write down what you know and what you want to find.

know A, a, C   want c

Write down the parts of the sine rule that you need.

$$\frac{a}{\sin A} = \frac{c}{\sin C}$$

$$\boxed{\frac{a}{\sin A}} = \frac{b}{\sin B} = \boxed{\frac{c}{\sin C}}$$

Substitute the values you know.

$$\frac{\ldots}{\sin 130°} = \frac{c}{\sin 35°}$$

$$\frac{12 \sin \ldots}{\sin 130°} = c$$

Solve for c.

$$c = \ldots\ldots\ldots\ldots\ldots = \ldots\ldots\ldots \text{ (to 1 d.p.)}$$

① **a** Calculate the length BC, correct to 1 d.p.

$b = 8\,cm$

b Calculate the length AB, correct to 1 d.p.

10 cm

② **a** Calculate the length DE, correct to 1 d.p.

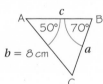

7.5 cm

b Work out the length x. Give your answer to the nearest cm.

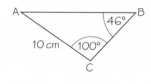

9 cm

Exam-style question

③ In triangle XYZ, ∠X = 50°, ∠Y= 100°, ∠Z = 30°, YZ = 15 cm.

Calculate the length XZ.

Give your answer to 3 significant figures.

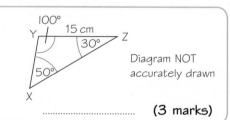

Diagram NOT accurately drawn

15 cm

(3 marks)

Reflect

Do you need to label all triangles ABC? Complete this version of the sine rule.

$$\frac{p}{\sin P} = \frac{q}{\sin \ldots} = \frac{\ldots}{\sin R}$$

2 Using the cosine rule and the area formula

When you know two sides and the included angle:
- use the cosine rule to find the other side
- use area $= \frac{1}{2} ab \sin C$ to find the area.

or

Guided practice

Calculate the length XZ,
correct to 1 d.p.

X 5 cm Y
40°
8 cm
Z

Label the angle you know A, the other
angles B and C and the sides a, b and c.

Write down the cosine rule.

$a^2 = b^2 + c^2 - 2bc \cos A$

$= 5^2 + \text{............}^2 - 2 \times \text{............} \times 8 \cos 40°$

$a^2 = 27.7164...$

$a = \text{............}$ cm (to 1 d.p.)

C X 5 cm Y A
b
40°
a
8 cm
c
B Z

> Label the angle A
> to match the formula.

> Find the square root.

① **a** Calculate the length BC, correct to 1 d.p.   **b** Calculate the length EF, correct to 1 d.p.

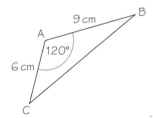

9 cm B
A
120°
6 cm
C

....

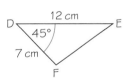

12 cm
D ———— E
45°
7 cm
F

....

② **a** On the triangle, label the angle you know C,
the other angles A and B, and
the sides a, b, and c.

b Substitute the values for a, b and C into

area $= \frac{1}{2} ab \sin C$ to calculate the area.

Give your answer to 1 d.p.

8 cm 60° 6 cm

Hint Label the angle C
to match the formula.

....

Exam-style question

③ The diagram shows triangle WXZ.

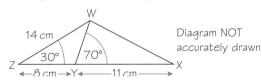

W
14 cm
30° 70°
Z ←8 cm→ Y ←——11 cm——→ X

Diagram NOT
accurately drawn

a Calculate the length WY.   .... (2 marks)

b Work out the area of triangle WXZ.   .... (2 marks)

Reflect   In Q2, when you label the angle you know C, does it matter which angle you label A
and which you label B?

③ Using the sine and cosine rules to find angles

To find angles, use the sine rule with 'angles on top'

$$\frac{\sin A}{a} = \frac{\sin B}{b} = \frac{\sin C}{c}$$

or

substitute into the cosine rule and solve to find angle A.

Guided practice

Calculate angle x, correct to 1 d.p.

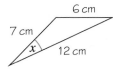

You know the two sides that include the angle, so use the cosine rule. Label the angle you want A.

$$a^2 = b^2 + c^2 - 2bc \cos A$$

$$6^2 = \text{...............} + \text{...............} - 2 \times 12 \times 7 \cos A$$

$$36 = \text{...............} - 168 \cos A$$

$$168 \cos A = \text{...............}$$

$$\cos A = \frac{\text{...............}}{168}$$

$$A = \cos^{-1}\left(\frac{\text{...............}}{\text{...............}}\right)$$

$$x = \text{.............................}° \text{ (to 1 d.p.)}$$

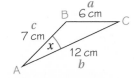

Label the angle A to match the formula.

---

① **a** Label the angle to be found (x) as A. Label C and the sides a, b and c.

b Use the sine rule to calculate $\sin A$. ....

c Hence work out angle A. ....

Hint

$$\frac{\sin A}{a} = \frac{\sin B}{b} = \frac{\sin C}{c}$$

② **a** Calculate angle Q, correct to 1 d.p.

b Calculate angle Y, to the nearest degree.

Hint Use the method in Q1.

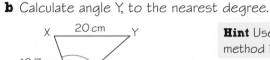

....

....

③ Use the cosine rule to work out angle y.

Hint $\cos y$ is negative.

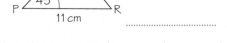

a   **b**

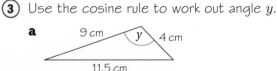

....

Exam-style question

④ The diagram shows triangle DEF.

a Calculate ∠D. .... **(2 marks)**

b Calculate ∠E. .... **(2 marks)**

D
6.9 cm
5.9 cm
E
Diagram NOT accurately drawn
F   7.6 cm

Reflect In Q4, when did you use the cosine rule? When did you use the sine rule?

4 Using area = $\frac{1}{2}ab\sin C$ to solve problems

When you know the area, you can use area = $\frac{1}{2}ab\sin C$ to find
- the angle between two given sides
- a side adjacent to a given angle.

Guided practice

Triangle PQR has area 21 cm².
Calculate ∠P, correct to 1 d.p.

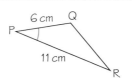

Label the angle you want C.

$$\text{Area} = \frac{1}{2}ab\sin C$$

$$21 = \frac{1}{2} \times \text{.............} \times \text{.............} \sin C$$

$$21 = \text{.............} \sin C$$

$$\frac{21}{\text{............}} = \sin C$$

$$C = \sin^{-1}\left(\frac{21}{\text{............}}\right) = \text{............}° \text{ (to 1 d.p.)}$$

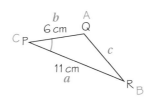

Label the angle to match the formula.

① **a** This triangle has area 35 cm².
Calculate the length a, correct to 1 d.p.

b This triangle has area 24 cm².
Calculate the length x, to 1 d.p.

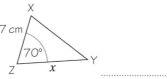

② **a** Triangle DEF has area 10 cm². Calculate angle x, correct to the nearest degree.

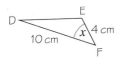

b Triangle HJK has area 20 cm². Calculate angle y.

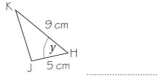

③ Triangle MNO is an isosceles triangle with area 7.7 cm².

a Calculate ∠O.

b Work out ∠N.

Give your answers to 1 d.p.

Exam-style question

④ Triangle STU is an isosceles triangle with area 62 cm².

Calculate angle x, correct to 1 d.p. .... **(3 marks)**

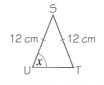

Diagram NOT accurately drawn

Reflect
In Q4, which angle facts did you use?

Practise the methods

Answer this question to check where to start.

Check up

Which is the correct working to find the length of side DF?

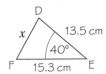

Ⓐ
$$\frac{15.3}{\sin D} = \frac{x}{\sin 40°} = \frac{13.5}{\sin F}$$

Ⓑ
$$x^2 = 13.5^2 + 15.3^2 - 2 \times 15.3 \times 13.5 \times \cos 40°$$

Ⓒ
$$x^2 = 15.3^2 + 13.5^2 + 2 \times 15.3 \times 13.5 \times \cos 40°$$

Ⓓ
$$x = \frac{1}{2} \times 13.5 \times 15.3 \times \sin 40°$$

If you ticked B go to Q2.   If you ticked A, C or D go to Q1.

① For each triangle
   i substitute the sides and angles given into the cosine rule and the sine rule
   ii decide which you can solve to work out x
   iii solve to calculate x, correct to 1 d.p.

a
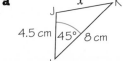

b
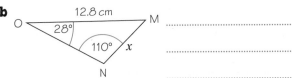

Exam-style questions

② Calculate the area of triangle XYZ.

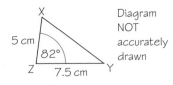

Diagram NOT accurately drawn

Give your answer to 1 d.p.   .... **(2 marks)**

③ The diagram shows triangle XYZ.

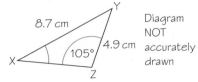

Diagram NOT accurately drawn

  a Calculate the size of ∠X.   .... **(2 marks)**

  b Work out the length of side XZ.   .... **(2 marks)**

④ Triangle ABC has area 9 cm^2.

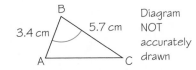

Diagram NOT accurately drawn

Calculate the size of angle B,
to the nearest degree.   .... **(3 marks)**

Get back
on track

Problem-solve!

Exam-style questions

(1) Calculate the area of an equilateral triangle with sides 6 cm.
Give your answer to 3 s.f. .... **(2 marks)**

(2) A boat sails 10 km due east from a harbour. It then sails on a bearing of 250° for 7 km, to a landing stage.

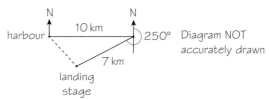

a Calculate the distance from the landing stage to the harbour (to 1 d.p.). .... **(2 marks)**

b What bearing should the boat sail on to return to the harbour (to the nearest degree)? .... **(2 marks)**

(3) Calculate the length of the shortest side of the triangle.

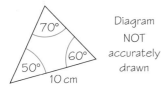

.... **(2 marks)**

(4) ABC is a right-angled triangle.
Calculate the area of the triangle.
Give your answer to 1 d.p.

Diagram NOT accurately drawn

.... **(3 marks)**

(5) The diagram shows a sector of a circle centre O, radius 6.8 cm.
The area of the sector is 12.11 cm² (to 2 d.p.).

Diagram NOT accurately drawn

a Calculate angle AOB. .... **(2 marks)**

b Calculate the area of triangle AOB. .... **(1 mark)**

c Hence work out the area of the segment bounded by AB, shown shaded on the diagram. .... **(1 mark)**

(6) ABCDE is a pyramid with square base of side 5 cm.
AD = AB = 9 cm.
Calculate the size of angle ADB correct to 1 d.p.

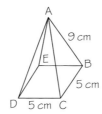

.... **(4 marks)**

Now that you have completed this unit, how confident do you feel?

| (1) Finding lengths using the sine rule | (2) Using the cosine rule and the area formula | (3) Using the sine and cosine rules to find angles | (4) Using area = ½ab sin C to solve problems |

Answers

1 Circle theorems

①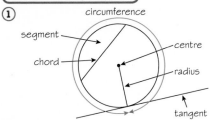

circumference

segment

centre

chord

radius

tangent

② **a** $x = 100°$ **b** $y = z = 55°$ **c** $a = 50°, b = 130°$

Confidence check

① $w = 50°$
② $x = 30°$
③ $y = 70°, z = 95°$
④ $t = 40°$

1 Angles at the centre and at the circumference

Guided practice

The angle at the centre is twice the angle at the circumference.
$\angle BOC = 2a$
$120° = 2a$
$60° = a$

① **a** $x = 65°$ **b** $y = 35°$ **c** $r = 80°$
d $s = 110°$ **e** $t = 250°$ **f** $u = 100°$
② **a** $90°$ **b** $90°$ **c** $90°$
③ $x = 120°$, angles around a point
$y = 60°$, angle at centre is twice angle at circumference
④ **a** $\angle DOF = 140°$, angle at the centre is twice the angle at the circumference
b $\angle ODE = 20°$ ⎫ base angles of
c $\angle OFD = 20°$ ⎬ isosceles triangle.
⑤ $a = 100°$ – angles at the centre are twice the angle at the circumference.
$a + b + 90 + 90 = 360°$ (angles in a quadrilateral, angle between radius and tangent = 90°) therefore $b = 180 - 100 = 80°$.
⑥ **a** $\angle JOK = 110°$, angle at the centre is twice the angle at the circumference
b $\angle OJT = 90°$, tangent meets radius at 90°
c $\angle OJK = 35°$, base angles of isosceles triangle
$\angle KJT = \angle OJT - \angle OJK = 90° - 35° = 55°$
d $TJ = TK$, tangents to a point are equal.
$\angle JTK = 180° - 55° - 55° = 70°$, angles in an isoceles triangle.
OR
$\angle JKT + \angle OJT + \angle JOK + \angle OKT = 360°$, angles in a quadrilateral
$\angle JTK + 90° + 110° + 90° = 360°$,
$\angle JTK = 70°$

2 Angles in the same segment

Guided practice

Angles in the same segment are equal.
$c = d = 40°$
① **a** $x = 30°$ **b** $y = 50°$ **c** $z = 70°$
② $r = 35°, s = 20°$

③ $\angle ABE = 110°$, vertically opposite angles
$\angle BEA = 40°$, angles in a triangle add up to 180°
$x = 40°$, angles in same segment are equal

3 Angles in a cyclic quadrilateral

Guided practice

Opposite angles in a cyclic quadrilateral add up to 180°.
$100° + x = 180°$
$x = 80°$
$70° + y = 180°$
$y = 110°$
① **a** $r = 60°$ **b** $s = 85°$
② **a** $\angle DCB = 80°$, opposite angles in cyclic quadrilaterals add up to 180°
b $\angle OPC = 90°$, a radius that bisects a chord meets the chord at 90°
c $\angle OCP = 30°$, angles in a triangle add up to 180°
d $\angle OCB = 80° - 30° = 50°$
③ $a = 70°$ (supplementary angles at parallel lines)
$b = 70°$ (base angles in a trapezium)
$c = 110°$ (opposite angles or base angles in a trapezium)

4 The alternate segment theorem

① **a** $p = 65°$ **b** $q = 70°$ **c** $r = 75°$
d $w = 40°, v = 60°$
② $a = b = 80°$
③ $\angle CAB = 45°$, alternate segment theorem
$x = 180° - 45° - 75° = 60°$, angles in triangle add up to 180°
OR
$\angle PBA = 75°$, alternate segment theorem
$x = 180° - 45° - 75° = 60°$, angles on a straight line

Practise the methods

① **a** $a = 90°$ **b** $b = 160°$ **c** $c = 180°$
② **a** $d = 40°, e = 20°$ **b** $f = 20°, g = 80°$
c $h = 50°, i = 100°$
③ **a** $j = 80°, k = 105°$ **b** $l = 90°, m = 40°, n = 40°$
c $p = 60°, q = 90°$
④ $x = 104°$, angle at centre is twice angle at circumference
$y = 38°$, base angle isosceles triangle
$z = 52°$, alternate segment theorem

Problem-solve!

① $\angle POR = 130°$, angles at point
$x = 65°$, angle at centre is twice angle at circumference
$y = 25°$, base angles in an isosceles triangle
② $c = 98°$
③ **a** $x = 90°$, angle in semicircle
$y = 30°$, angles in a triangle add up to 180°
$z = 60°$, opposite angles in cyclic quadrilateral add up to 180°
b $\angle ADC = 90°$, so triangles ABC and ADC are congruent/identical
④ $\angle ABF = \angle DCF = 36°$, angles in the same segment,
$\angle BAF = \angle BFA = 72°$, base angles in an isosceles triangle,
$a = 27°$, angles on a straight line total 180°
⑤ $c = 60°$, angles in the alternate segment are equal, the angle in a semicircle is 90° and angles on straight line add up to 180°

2 Manipulating algebra

AO1 Fluency check

1. **a** x^5　　**b** x^2　　**c** $6a + 3b - 2b^2$
2. **a** $8x^2 - 2x$　　**b** $x^3 + 3x^2$
   c $x^2 - 3x - 4$　　**d** $-3x^2 - 12$
   e $x^2 + 10x^2 + 25$　　**f** $x^2 - 4$
3. **a** $(x - 3)(x + 3)$　　**b** $(x - 8)(x + 8)$
   c $(x + 2)(x + 3)$
4. **a** $\dfrac{9}{10}$　　**b** $\dfrac{6}{35}$　　**c** $\dfrac{3}{2}$ or $1\dfrac{1}{2}$

5. **Number sense**

   a Various answers including: 1 and 24
   b Various answers including: 3 and 8
   c Various answers including: −4 and −6

Confidence check

1. $6x^2 + 11x + 3$
2. $(2x - 1)(2x + 5)$
3. $x^3 + 3x^2 + 3$
4. $\dfrac{7x}{12}$

1 Expanding double brackets

Guided practice

$$(2x + 3)(3x + 2) = 2x(3x + 2) + 3(3x + 2)$$
$$= 6x^2 + 4x + 9x + 6$$
$$= 6x^2 + 13x + 6$$

1. **a** $6x^2 + 11x + 4$　　**b** $8x^2 + 16x - 10$
   c $12x^2 - 5x - 2$
2. **a** $10x^2 + x - 3$　　**b** $12x^2 - 19x + 5$
   c $10x^2 - 23x + 12$
3. **a** $25x^2 - 9$　　**b** $16x^2 - 49$
   c $9x^2 - 1$
4. $(4x - 3)(4x - 3) = 4x(4x - 3) - 3(4x - 3)$
   $= 16x^2 - 12x - 12x + 9$
   $= 16x^2 - 24x + 9$
5. $4x^2 + 12x + 9$

2 Factorising quadratic expressions of the form $ax^2 + bx + c$

Guided practice

$$2x^2 + 4x + 5x + 10 = 2x(x + 2) + 5(x + 2)$$
$$= (2x + 5)(x + 2)$$

1. **a** $(3x + 2)(x + 4)$　　**b** $(x + 2)(2x + 3)$
   c $(2x + 1)(5x + 2)$
2. **a** $(2x + 2)(x - 3)$　　**b** $(3x - 2)(x + 5)$
3. **a** $(3x - 2)(x - 4)$　　**b** $(2x - 3)(2x - 5)$
   c $(2x - 1)(4x - 3)$
4. **a** $(3x - 2)(3x + 2)$　　**b** $(12x - 7)(12x + 7)$
5. $(3x + 1)(2x + 5)$

3 Simplifying expressions with brackets and powers

1. **a** $6a + 14b$　　**b** $13x + 11y$
   c $-7e$　　**d** $4z - 6t$
2. **a** $x^3 + 3x^2 + 4x$　　**b** $x^3 - 2x^2 + x$
   c $a^4 + 2a^3 - 3a^2$　　**d** $4y^3 - y^5 + 2y^4$
3. **a** $x^3 + 2x^2 + 3x$　　**b** $m^3 - 3m^2 + 7m - 7$
   c $x^3 + x^2 + 5x - 12$　　**d** $y^3 - 2y^2 + 12y - 21$
4. **a** $x^2 + 4x + 9$　　**b** $x^2 - 5x + 14$
   c $4a^2 + 16a + 9$　　**d** $9p^2 + 4p - 2$
5. **a** $x^3 + 3x^2 + 2x$　　**b** $y^3 + 2y^2 - 3y$
6. **a** $y^3 + 6y^2 + 9y$　　**b** $x^3 - 4x^2 + 4x$
   c $a^3 + 8a^2 + 13a$　　**d** $x^3 + 2x^2 - x - 3$
7. **a** $x^3 + 3x^2 + 5x + 3$　　**b** $x^3 - x^2 - 3x + 2$
   c $x^3 + x^2 - 10x + 8$
8. **a** $x^3 + 3x^2 - 6x - 8$　　**b** $x^3 - 7x - 6$
   c $y^3 + 4y^2 + y - 6$

9. $x^3 + 5x^2 + 3x - 9$

4 Simplifying expressions involving algebraic fractions

1. **a** $\dfrac{2x}{y}$　　**b** $\dfrac{x^4 y}{2}$　　**c** $\dfrac{2}{y}$
2. **a** $\dfrac{2x}{3}$　　**b** $\dfrac{3x}{10}$　　**c** $\dfrac{13x}{12}$
3. **a** $\dfrac{x + 12}{4}$　　**b** $\dfrac{3x - 1}{8}$
4. **a** $x + 2$　　**b** $\dfrac{1}{x - 3}$　　**c** $\dfrac{2}{x + 1}$
5. $\dfrac{x + 2}{x - 5}$

Practise the methods

1. **a** $4x^2 + 8x + 3$　　**b** $4x^2 + 20x + 25$
   c $4x^2 + 16x + 16$
2. **a** $3a - 15b$　　**b** $4x^2 - 10x - 10$
3. **a** $x^3 + 3x^2 - 4x$　　**b** $y^3 - 2y^2 + 5y$
4. **a** $x^3 + 6x^2 + 5x$　　**b** $x^3 - x^2 - 6x$
5. **a** $x^3 - x^2 - 14x + 24$　　**b** $x^3 - 3x^2 - 9x - 5$
6. **a** $\dfrac{2m}{15}$　　**b** $\dfrac{7x}{18}$　　**c** $\dfrac{29x}{21}$
7. **a** $\dfrac{x + 5}{2}$　　**b** $\dfrac{3}{x - 3}$
8. **a** $\dfrac{2xy^2}{3}$　　**b** $\dfrac{2n + 1}{2n + 3}$

Problem-solve!

1. $(3x + 5)(2x - 3) = 6x^2 - 9x + 10x - 15$
   $= 6x^2 + x - 15$
2. $(2x + 1)^2 - 2(x + 1)^2$
   $= (2x + 1)(2x + 1) - 2(x + 1)(x + 1)$
   $= 4x^2 + 2x + 2x + 1 - 2(x^2 + x + x + 1)$
   $= 4x^2 + 4x + 1 - 2(x^2 + 2x + 1)$
   $= 4x^2 + 4x + 1 - 2x^2 - 4x - 2$
   $= 2x^2 - 1$ as required
3. $(x + 2)^3$
   $= (x + 2)(x + 2)(x + 2)$
   $= (x + 2)(x^2 + 2x + 2x + 4)$
   $= x(x^2 + 4x + 4) + 2(x^2 + 4x + 4)$
   $= x^3 + 4x^2 + 4x + 2x^2 + 8x + 8$
   $= x^3 + 6x^2 + 12x + 8$
4. **a** $x^3 - x^2 - x + 1$　　**b** $x^3 - 3x^2 - 25x + 75$
5. $5x^2 + 9x - 5$
6. $2x^3 + 3x^2 - 2x - 3$
7. $\dfrac{x - 2}{x + 2}$
8. **a** $(2x + 1)(x + 3)$　　**b** $\dfrac{2x + 1}{x - 3}$

3 Solving quadratic equations

AO1 Fluency check

1. **a** $(x - 3)(x + 4)$　　**b** $(x - 4)(x + 4)$
   c $(2x + 3)(x + 6)$
2. **a** $x^2 + 10x + 25$　　**b** $x^2 - 14x + 49$
   c $x^2 + 8x + 16$
3. **a** $x = -2 + 8 = 6$ and $x = -2 - 8 = -10$
   b $x = 3 + \sqrt{5}$ and $x = 3 - \sqrt{5}$
   c $x = -1 + \sqrt{2}$ and $x = -1 - \sqrt{2}$

4. **Number sense**

$a = 0, b = 5$; $a = 7, b = 0$; $a = \sqrt{2}, b = 0$; $a = 0, b = 0$

Confidence check

1. $x = 2$ or $x = -3$
2. $x = -4 + \sqrt{5}$ or $x = -4 - \sqrt{5}$
3. $x = \dfrac{-3 + \sqrt{29}}{2}$ or $x = \dfrac{-3 - \sqrt{29}}{2}$

1 Solving quadratic equations by factorising

Guided practice

$$x^2 - x - 6 = 0$$
$$(x + 2)(x - 3) = 0$$
So $x + 2 = 0$ or $x - 3 = 0$
$$x = -2 \text{ or } x = 3$$

① **a** $x = -4$ or $x = 2$ **b** $x = -3$ or $x = 5$
   c $x = -7$ or $x = -2$

② **a** $x = -2$ (repeated)   **b** $x = 3$ (repeated)
   c $x = 7$ (repeated)   **d** $x = -4$ or $x = 4$
   e $x = -5$ or $x = 5$ **f** $x = -4$ or $x = 4$

③ **a** $x = 0$ or $x = 8$ **b** $x = 0$ or $x = -3$
   c $x = 0$ or $x = \dfrac{5}{2}$

④ $y = 4$ or $y = -7$

⑤ **a** $x = -1$ or $x = 4$ **b** $x = -2$ or $x = 5$
   c $x = -3$ or $x = 7$

2 Solving quadratic equations by completing the square

Guided practice

$$\begin{array}{c} (x + 2)^2 = x^2 + 4x + 4 \\ (x + 2)^2 - 3 = x^2 + 4x + 1 \end{array}$$
$-3 \quad\quad\quad\quad\quad\quad\quad\quad\quad\quad -3$

Solve $(x + 2)^2 - 3 = 0$
$$(x + 2)^2 = 3$$
$$x + 2 = \pm\sqrt{3}$$
$$x + 2 = \sqrt{3} \text{ or } x + 2 = -\sqrt{3}$$
$$x = -2 + \sqrt{3} \text{ or } x = -2 - \sqrt{3}$$

① **a** $x^2 + 2x + 1$ **b** $x^2 - 2x + 1$
   c $x^2 + 6x + 9$ **d** $x^2 - 4x + 4$

② **a** $(x + 1)^2$ **b** $(x - 1)^2$

③ **a** $x = 1$ or $x = -3$ **b** $x = 1 + \sqrt{5}$ or $x = 1 - \sqrt{5}$
   c $x = -1$ or $x = -5$ **d** $x = 2 + \sqrt{6}$ or $x = 2 - \sqrt{6}$
   e $x = -5 - \sqrt{3}$ or $x = -5 + \sqrt{3}$
   f $x = 4 + \sqrt{2}$ or $x = 4 - \sqrt{2}$

④ $x = 3 + \sqrt{7}$ or $x = 3 - \sqrt{7}$

3 Solving quadratic equations by using the quadratic formula

Guided practice

$x^2 + 5x - 7 = 0$
$a = 1 \quad b = 5 \quad c = -7$
Substitute for a, b and c in the quadratic formula.
$$x = \frac{-b \pm\sqrt{b^2 - 4ac}}{2a}$$
$$x = \frac{-5 \pm\sqrt{5^2 - 4 \times 1 \times -7}}{2 \times 1}$$
$$x = \frac{-5 \pm\sqrt{25 + 28}}{2}$$
$$x = \frac{-5 \pm\sqrt{53}}{2}$$
Use your calculator.
$x = 1.14$ or $x = -6.14$

① **a** $x = -2.62$ or $x = -0.38$
   b $x = -0.44$ or $x = -4.56$
   c $x = 2.38$ or $x = 4.62$
   d $x = -4.19$ or $x = 1.19$
   e $x = 5.70$ or $x = -0.70$
   f $x = -9.72$ or $x = 0.72$

② **a** $x = \dfrac{1 + \sqrt{21}}{2}$ or $x = \dfrac{1 - \sqrt{21}}{2}$

   b $x = \dfrac{-7 + \sqrt{33}}{2}$ or $x = \dfrac{-7 - \sqrt{33}}{2}$

   c $x = \dfrac{-5 + \sqrt{13}}{2}$ or $x = \dfrac{-5 - \sqrt{13}}{2}$

③ $x = 0.382$ or $x = 2.62$

Practise the methods

① **a** $x = 3$ or $x = 6$ **b** $x = -2$ or $x = -5$
   c $x = 2$ or $x = -5$

② **a** $x = 3$ or $x = -1$
   b $x = -4 + \sqrt{10}$ or $x = -4 - \sqrt{10}$
   c $x = 5 + \sqrt{7}$ or $x = 5 - \sqrt{7}$

③ **a** $x = -0.35$ or $x = -5.65$
   b $x = 7.32$ or $x = 0.68$
   c $x = 6.27$ or $x = -1.27$

④ $x = 1.87$ or $x = -5.87$

⑤ $x = 1 \pm \sqrt{6}$

Problem-solve!

① $x^2 + 3x - 10 = 0$

② $x = 4$ (repeated)

③ $x = -4.52$ or $x = -15.5$

④ $x = 4$ and $x + 7 = 11$

⑤ $x = \dfrac{7}{2}$ cm or 3.5 cm

⑥ $x = \dfrac{-1 + \sqrt{19}}{3}$ or $x = \dfrac{-1 - \sqrt{19}}{3}$

⑦ **a** $x = \dfrac{-5 + 3\sqrt{5}}{2}$ or $x = \dfrac{-5 - 3\sqrt{5}}{2}$

   b $x = -1 + \sqrt{5}$ or $x = -1 - \sqrt{5}$
   c $x = 2 + \sqrt{10}$ or $x = 2 - \sqrt{10}$

4 Algebraic graphs

A01 Fluency check

①

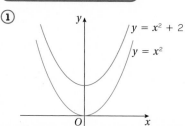

② **a** 3   **b** $-\dfrac{1}{2}$ **c** $\dfrac{-3}{2}$

③ **a** $x = -4$ or $x = 1$ **b** $x = 2$ or $x = -7$

④ **a** $x = -0.3$, $x = -3.7$ **b** $x = -1.4$, $x = 3.4$

⑤ **Number sense**

   a 4   **b** 1   **c** -3

Confidence check

① $y = -\dfrac{1}{2}x + 1$

②

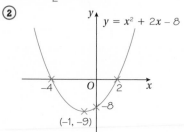

③ $x < -4$ and $x > 2$

1 Equations of parallel and perpendicular lines

Guided practice

a $y = 3x + c$
    $10 = 3 \times 2 + c$
    $c = 4$
Equation is $y = 3x + 4$

b $y = -\frac{1}{3}x + c$

$-5 = -\frac{1}{3} \times 3 + c$

$c = -4$

Equation is $y = -\frac{1}{3}x - 4$

(1) **a** $y = 2x + 1$　　　　**b** $y = -x - 2$

(2) **a** $y = -\frac{1}{2}x + 3$　　　**b** $y = \frac{1}{4}x + 1$

(3) $y = 10 - \frac{3}{2}x$

(4) $y = 5x + 2$

2 Using factorising to sketch quadratic graphs

(1) **a** $(3, -4)$　**b** $(1, -16)$

(2) **a** $(0, 5)$　**b** $(0, -15)$

(3)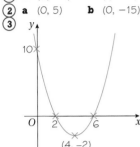

(4) **a** $(0, 3)$　**b** $x = 3$ and $x = 1$　**c** $(2, -1)$

d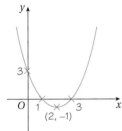

(5)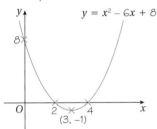

(6)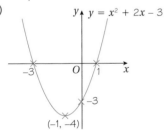

3 Using completing the square to sketch quadratic graphs

$(x + 3)^2 = 1$

$(x + 3) = \sqrt{1}$

$x + 3 = \pm 1$

Roots: $x = -2$ and $x = -4$

$(x + 3)^2 - 1$

$a = 1, b = 3, c = -1$

Turning point $= (-b, c) = (-3, -1)$

(1) Roots: $x = -1$ and $x = -3$　Turning point: $(-2, -1)$

(2) Roots: $x = -6.4$ and $x = 1.6$

Turning point: $(-4, 6)$　y-intercept: $(0, 10)$

(3)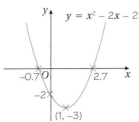

(4) $y = -(x - 3)^2 + 2$

Roots: $x = \sqrt{2} + 3$ and $-\sqrt{2} + 3$, or 4.41... and 1.59...

Turning point: $(3, 2)$

4 Solving quadratic inequalities

(1) **a** $-3 < x < 1$　　　　**b** $x < 1$ and $x > 4$

(2) $-1 \le x \le 5$

(3) $x \le -3$ and $x \ge 6$

Practise the methods

(1) **a** Roots: $x = 2$ and $x = 3$;　y-intercept: $(0, 6)$

b Roots: $x = 3$ and $x = -4$;　y-intercept: $(0, -12)$

(2) $y = 4x + 5$

(3) $y = 2x - 5$

(4) **a** $x = -2$ and $x = 6$

b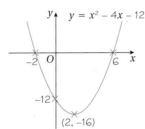

(5) **a** Roots: $x = 4.6$ and $x = -0.6$

b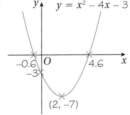

(6) $-1 < x < 3$

Problem-solve!

(1) **a** $y = 2x + 5$　　　　　**b** $y = -\frac{1}{2}x + 5$

(2) **a** $y = x + 12$　　　　　**b** $y = 4$

c $y = \frac{1}{7}x + \frac{20}{7}$

(3)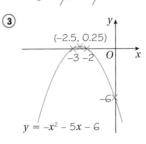

(4) $(\frac{1}{2}, -\frac{9}{4})$

(5) $x < -\frac{1}{2}$ and $x > 4$

5 Sequences

(1) **a** 3, 7, 11, 15   **b** 20, 15, 10, 5
    c 4, 8, 16, 32   **d** 1000, 100, 10, 1
(2) **a** + 7   **b** − 3
(3) **a** 3, 5, 7, 9; 10th term 21
    b −5, −2, 1, 4; 10th term 22

(4) Number sense

   a $\times \frac{1}{2}$, ÷ 2
   b + 3, × 2
   c − 8, ÷ 3, $\times \frac{1}{3}$

Confidence check

(1) 6, 3, 1.5
(2) **a** arithmetic   **b, c** geometric
(3) $2n^2 + 1$

1 Continuing sequences

Guided practice

a arithmetic sequence, term-to-term rule is divide by 2
b Term-to-term rule is multiply by 1.4.
(1) **a** 30, 20, 10, arithmetic, subtract 10
    b 48, 96, 192, geometric, multiply by 2
    c 1, $\frac{1}{4}$, $\frac{1}{16}$, geometric, divide by 4 (or multiply by $\frac{1}{4}$)
(2) **a** B, C   **b** A   **c** A, C
    d B   **e** A, C   **f** B
(3) **a** 4, $4\sqrt{2}$ **b** $12\sqrt{3}$, 36
(4) **a** × 1.2   **b** £1244.16

2 Quadratic sequences

Guided practice

nth term = $2n^2 + 3n + 1$
(1) **a** 29, 41, 55   **b** 26, 37, 50
    c 12, 6, −1   **d** −4, −8, −9
(2) **a** 7, 10, 15, 22   **b** 3, 10, 21, 36
    c −3, 3, 15, 27   **d** 4, 15, 34, 61
(3) **a** $4n^2 + n + 2$ **b** $2n^2 + 3n$
(4) **a** $n^2 − 2n + 1$; 10th term 81
    b $2n^2 + 7$; 10th term 207
(5) $n^2 + 5n − 2$

3 Pattern sequences

Guided practice

a $n(n + 2)$ **b** 10(10 + 2) = 120
(1) **a** $n(n + 1)$ **b** $\frac{1}{2}n(n + 1)$
(2) $\frac{1}{2}n(n + 1)$

Practise the methods

(1) **a**   **i** 1, 4, 9, 16   **ii** 2, 8, 18, 32
      iii 3, 12, 27, 48   **iv** 4, 16, 36, 64
    b   **i** 3, 5, 7; 2   **ii** 6, 10, 14; 4
      iii 9, 15, 21; 6   **iv** 12, 20, 28; 8
      2nd difference = 2 × number in front of n^2 in general term
(2) **a** $2n^2 + 2n$ **b** $2n^2 − 2n$ **c** No

---

(3) **a**   **b** n^2 **c** $n^2 + 2$

(4) **a** × 1.5
    b 3417.1875

Problem-solve!

(1) **a** 16, 5.$\dot{3}$ **b** 43.52, 69.632
(2) Any PIN that obeys the rules, e.g. 1234 or 2468 or 1248 or 0246
(3) **a** finite   **b** infinite
(4) $\frac{3}{\sqrt{3}} = \frac{3\sqrt{3}}{3} = \sqrt{3}$, $\frac{\sqrt{3}}{\sqrt{3}} = 1$
(5) £7460
(6) nth term $3n^2 + 5$, 9th term = 248
(7) $\frac{1}{2}n^2 + \frac{1}{2}n$, or $\frac{1}{2}n(n + 1)$

6 Congruence and similarity

(1) **a** 2   **b** 3
(2) **a** 35°, vertically opposite angles
    b 110°, alternate angles
    c 70°, corresponding angles

(3) Number sense

   a 5, 1.2   **b** 8, 2.5

Confidence check

(1) A, B, E
(2) ∠AEB = ∠ADB (corresponding angles)
    ∠ABE = ∠ACE (corresponding angles)
    ∠A is common to both. Triangles ABE and ACD are similar because they have the same angles.
(3) 100 cm²
(4) 9 cm

1 Deciding if shapes are congruent or similar

Guided practice

a C (ASA or SAS)   **b** B
(1) **a** ASA   **b** RHS or SSA
    c SSA   **d** SSS or SAS
(2) $x = z = 98°$, $y = 37°$, $p = 5.2$ cm, $q = 6.1$ cm
(3) **a** B is enlargement of A, scale factor 2.
      For hypotenuses in B and C scale factor is 1.5.
      (10 × 1.5 = 15)
      For shorter sides in B and C, scale factor is 1.33. (6 × 1.333 = 8)
      C is not an enlargement of B, so they are not similar.
(4) **a** FE = 14.4 cm   **b** AC = 13 cm
(5) ASA

2 Proving that triangles are similar

Guided practice

∠ABC = ∠ADE = x corresponding angles
∠ACB = ∠AED = y corresponding angles
∠BAC and ∠DAE are the same angle.
Triangles ABC and ADE are similar because they have equal angles.
(1) ∠V = 40°, ∠VXW = 90° = ∠VZY
    ∠VWX = ∠VYZ = 180 − 90 − 40 = 50°, (angle sum of a triangle)

(2) Scale factor of enlargement is 1.25 for each pair of corresponding sides.

(3) **a** ∠STU = ∠UVW, alternate angles
∠UST = ∠UWV, alternate angles
∠SUT = ∠VUW, vertically opposite angles
UW = 2 × TU = 10 cm

3 Perimeters and areas of enlargement

Guided practice

a Perimeter of rectangle = 2 + 4 + 2 + 4 = 12 cm
Perimeter of enlargement = 3 × 12 = 36 cm

b Area of rectangle = 2 × 4 = 8 cm²
Area of enlargement = 3² × 8 = 9 × 8 = 72 cm²

(1) **a**

	6	
		2

b rectangle: 8; enlargement: 16

(2) **a** 32 cm   **b** 64 cm²

(3) **a** 2.5   **b** 43.75 cm²

(4) 45 cm²

4 Similar shapes

Guided practice

∠AEB = ∠CED, same angle
∠ABE = ∠CDE = 90° given
AB and CD are parallel, because ∠ABE and ∠CDE are corresponding angles.
∠EAB = ∠ECD, corresponding angles
Triangles ABE and CDE are similar because they have equal angles.
AE = 3 + 5 = 8 cm
5 × scale factor = 8
Scale factor = $\frac{8}{5}$ = 1.6
DE = 6 ÷ 1.6 = 3.75 cm

(1) **a** ∠P = ∠P, ∠PQT = ∠PRS = 90°, TQ and SR are parallel.
∠PTQ = ∠PSR, corresponding angles.

b 5 cm

(2) **a** ∠ACB = ∠DCE, vertically opposite angles.
∠CAB = ∠CED and ∠CBA = ∠CDE, alternate angles

b 4 cm

(3) **a** AC = 12, BC = 6   **b** 1.5
c PD = 4, AD = 8   **d** P(9, 5)

(4) include proof of similarity
a 6 cm   **b** 1 cm

(5) $\frac{ED}{AD}$ or $\frac{EC}{AB}$

Practise the methods

(1) **a** ∠H = 20°, ∠K = 40°, ∠I = 120°, ∠J = 120°

b

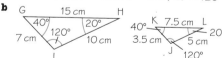

c JK = 3.5 cm

(2) RHS

(3) ∠U = 25°, ∠UVT = ∠URS = 110°, and
∠UTV = ∠USR, corresponding angles

(4) 36 cm²

(5) **a** ∠VWX = 30° (alternate angles)

b ∠VWX = ∠WYZ, ∠YXZ = VXW, ∠XVW = ∠XZY (alternate angles). Triangles VWX and XYZ have same angles and so are similar.

c XY = 1.5 cm

Problem-solve!

(1) ∠ACB = 80°, angles in triangle sum to 180°
∠DCE = 80°, vertically opposite, ∠EDC = 60° and ·
∠DEC = 40°, alternate angles. BC = CD = 8 cm.
ABC and CDE are congruent, SAS.

(2) a = 50°, b = 100°, c = 6 cm, d = 5 cm

(3) 900 cm²

(4) 20 cm²

(5) **a**

b 1 cm³   8 cm³   **c** 2³

(6) **a** B is an enlargement of A with factor 3.
b 33.5 × 3³ = 904.5 cm³

7 Right-angled triangles

AO1 Fluency check

(1) **a** 0.643   **b** 1   **c** 0.174   **d** 2.747

(2) **a** 11.5°   **b** 36.9°   **c** 34.1°   **d** 71.6°

(3) **a** x = 60   **b** $x = \frac{1}{2}$ **c** $x = \frac{2}{3}$

(4) **a** 10.3 cm   **b** 4.1 cm

Confidence check

(1) 7.2 cm   (2) 63.6°   (3) 11 cm   (4) 6.6 cm

1 Finding lengths in right-angled triangles

Guided practice

x = 5.297685557 = 5.3 cm (to 1 d.p.)

(1) **a** 6.8 cm   **b** 5.0 cm

(2) **a** 4.5 cm   **b** 6.8 cm

(3) **a** 6.7 cm   **b** 7.0 cm

(4) **a** 3.5 cm   **b** 5.6 cm   **c** 4.1 cm

(5) 211 cm

2 Finding angles in right-angled triangles

Guided practice

$w = \sin^{-1}\left(\frac{5}{8}\right)$ = 38.7° (to 1 d.p.)

(1) **a** m = 25.4°   **b** m = 33.7°

(2) **a** t = 36°   **b** s = 64°

(3) **a** x = 76°   **b** y = 14°

(4) 21.8°

3 Using trigonometry to solve problems

Guided practice

x = 9.1 cm (to 1 d.p.)

(1) **a** 12.4 cm   **b** 16.6 cm   **c** 6.4 cm   **d** 33.3 mm

(2) **a** 5 m   **b** 1.3 m

(3) 49 cm

(4) **a** 20° (alternate angles)   **b** 110 m or 109.9 m

4 Using Pythagoras' theorem in 3D problems

Guided practice

FH = $\sqrt{52}$ = 7.211... cm
d = $\sqrt{77}$ = 8.774964387 = 8.8 cm (to 1 d.p.)

(1) **a** 8.6 cm   **b**   **c** 10.5 cm

(2) 7.3 cm
(3) 5.2 cm
(4) 5 cm
(5) 117 mm

Practise the methods

(1) **a** **i** $y^2 = 10^2 + 7^2$, $y = \sqrt{10^2 + 7^2}$

  ii $\sin 55° = \dfrac{10}{y}$, $y = \dfrac{10}{\sin 55°}$

  iii $\cos 55° = \dfrac{7}{y}$, $y = \dfrac{7}{\cos 55°}$

  b $y = 12.2$ cm

(2) **a** $r = 36.9°$ **b** $s = 2.9$ cm

  c $t = 39.3°$, $u = 50.7°$ **d** $w = 6.6$ m, $v = 7.0$ m

(3) 28.9 m

(4) 17.3 cm

Problem-solve!

(1) 56.4°

(2) **a** 119.7° or 120°   **b** 8.06 km

(3) 12 m

(4) No, maximum length = diagonal = 21 cm

(5) **a**   **b** AD = $\sqrt{3}$ cm

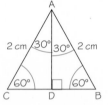

  c **i** $\cos 60° = \dfrac{1}{2}$ **ii** $\sin 60° = \dfrac{\sqrt{3}}{2}$

  iii $\cos 30° = \dfrac{\sqrt{3}}{2}$ **iv** $\sin 30° = \dfrac{1}{2}$

8 Trigonometry in non-right-angled triangles

A01 Fluency check

(1)

(2) **a** $c = \dfrac{10}{7}$ **b** $d = \dfrac{3}{2}$ **c** $e = 3$

(3) **a** 59.0°   **b** 22.0°   **c** 44.4°   **d** 77.2°

(4) Number sense

  a $\dfrac{3}{2} = \dfrac{6}{4}$ **b** Yes

Confidence check

(1) 7.8 cm   **(2)** 70.9°   **(3)** 14.1 cm²

1 Finding lengths using the sine rule

Guided practice

$c = 9.0$ cm (to 1 d.p.)

(1) **a** 6.5 cm   **b** 13.7 cm

(2) **a** 3.8 cm   **b** 11 cm

(3) 19.3 cm

2 Using the cosine rule and the area formula

Guided practice

$a = 5.3$ cm (to 1 d.p.)

(1) **a** 13.0 cm   **b** 8.6 cm

(2) **a**

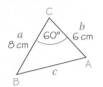 or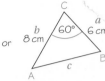

  b 20.8 cm²

(3) **a** 7.4 cm   **b** 66.5 cm²

3 Using the sine and cosine rules to find angles

Guided practice

$x = 20.8°$ (to 1 d.p.)

(1) **a**

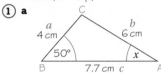

  b 0.5107... **c** 30.7°

(2) **a** 76.5°   **b** 40°

(3) **a** 120°   **b** 80°

(4) **a** 72.4°   **b** 47.7°

4 Using area = $\frac{1}{2}ab\sin C$ to solve problems

Guided practice

$C = 39.5°$ (to 1 d.p.)

(1) **a** 10.2 cm   **b** 7.3 cm

(2) **a** 30°   **b** 62.7°

(3) **a** 74.3°   **b** 52.9°

(4) 60.3°

Practise the methods

(1) **a** 5.8 cm   **b** 6.4 cm

(2) 18.6 cm²

(3) **a** 33°   **b** 6 cm

(4) 68°

Problem-solve!

(1) 15.6 cm²

(2) **a** 4.2 km   **b** 305°

(3) 8.2 cm

(4) area = 18.9 cm²

(5) **a** 30°   **b** 11.56 cm²   **c** 0.55 cm²

(6) 46.2°